ENVIRONMENTAL REMEDIATION TECHNOLOGIES,
REGULATIONS AND SAFETY

EPA'S PROPOSED CARBON DIOXIDE RULE FOR EXISTING POWER PLANTS

ELEMENTS AND IMPLICATIONS

ENVIRONMENTAL REMEDIATION TECHNOLOGIES, REGULATIONS AND SAFETY

Additional books in this series can be found on Nova's website under the Series tab.

Additional e-books in this series can be found on Nova's website under the e-book tab.

ENVIRONMENTAL REMEDIATION TECHNOLOGIES,
REGULATIONS AND SAFETY

EPA'S PROPOSED CARBON DIOXIDE RULE FOR EXISTING POWER PLANTS

ELEMENTS AND IMPLICATIONS

CARMELLA RAMOS
EDITOR

nova publishers
New York

For permission to use material from this book please contact us:
Telephone 631-231-7269; Fax 631-231-8175
Web Site: http://www.novapublishers.com

NOTICE TO THE READER

The Publisher has taken reasonable care in the preparation of this book, but makes no expressed or implied warranty of any kind and assumes no responsibility for any errors or omissions. No liability is assumed for incidental or consequential damages in connection with or arising out of information contained in this book. The Publisher shall not be liable for any special, consequential, or exemplary damages resulting, in whole or in part, from the readers' use of, or reliance upon, this material. Any parts of this book based on government reports are so indicated and copyright is claimed for those parts to the extent applicable to compilations of such works.

Independent verification should be sought for any data, advice or recommendations contained in this book. In addition, no responsibility is assumed by the publisher for any injury and/or damage to persons or property arising from any methods, products, instructions, ideas or otherwise contained in this publication.

This publication is designed to provide accurate and authoritative information with regard to the subject matter covered herein. It is sold with the clear understanding that the Publisher is not engaged in rendering legal or any other professional services. If legal or any other expert assistance is required, the services of a competent person should be sought. FROM A DECLARATION OF PARTICIPANTS JOINTLY ADOPTED BY A COMMITTEE OF THE AMERICAN BAR ASSOCIATION AND A COMMITTEE OF PUBLISHERS.

Additional color graphics may be available in the e-book version of this book.

Library of Congress Cataloging-in-Publication Data

ISBN: 978-1-63463-178-5

Published by Nova Science Publishers, Inc. † New York

CONTENTS

Preface   **vii**

Chapter 1   EPA's Proposed Greenhouse Gas
                 Regulations:Implications for the Electric
                 Power Sector   **1**
                 Richard J. Campbell

Chapter 2   State CO_2 Emission Rate Goals in EPA's Proposed
                 Rule for Existing Power Plants   **27**
                 Jonathan L. Ramseur

Chapter 3   EPA's Proposed Greenhouse Gas
                 Regulations for Existing Power Plants:
                 Frequently Asked Questions   **61**
                 James E. McCarthy, Robert Meltz, Jane A. Leggett,
                 Jonathan L. Ramseur and Alissa M. Dolan

Chapter 4   EPA Regulation of Greenhouse Gases:
                 Congressional Responses and Options   **91**
                 James E. McCarthy

Chapter 5   By the Numbers:
                 Cutting Carbon Pollution from Power Plants   **115**
                 Environmental Protection Agency

Index   **119**

PREFACE

This book discusses the implications for the electric power sector. It also examines the carbon dioxide emission rate goals in EPA's proposed rule for existing power plants; and discusses the Congressional responses and options to the EPA regulation of greenhouse gases.

Chapter 1 - The Environmental Protection Agency (EPA) has proposed regulations to reduce greenhouse gas (GHG) emissions from existing power plants. EPA believes that its proposed Clean Power Plan (CPP) will "protect public health, move the United States towards a cleaner environment, and fight climate change while supplying Americans with reliable and affordable power." Burning fossil fuels to produce electricity results in the release of carbon dioxide, and represents the largest source of GHG emissions in the United States. Under its proposed plan, EPA believes it will be possible to lower the carbon intensity of power generation in the United States by approximately 30% in 2030 from carbon dioxide emissions levels in 2005. To achieve this goal, EPA is giving each state a numerical carbon reduction target, based on the state's existing power generation portfolio.

Under the Clean Air Act (CAA) section 111(d), the EPA must identify the best system of emission reductions (BSER) that is adequately demonstrated and available to reduce pollution. The regulations allow EPA to set goals, and give states the responsibility for creating compliance plans which meet those goals. EPA set the state-specific goals based on (1) measures which improve the efficiency of fossil-fueled power plants, (2) use of lower-emitting generation sources such as natural gas or fuel-switching to natural gas, and use of nuclear power, (3) demand-side efficiency, and (4) renewable electric generation. EPA has suggested these measures as four BSER "building blocks" or options for states to consider when choosing how to meet their specific GHG reduction goals. Under the proposed plan, however, states would have the flexibility to choose the most cost-effective strategies to meet the targets.

EPA's proposal for GHG reduction answers some questions from the electric power sector with regard to the timeframe, timeline, and choices that would be made available for compliance. The CPP proposal sets out a vision for a greater proportion of electricity coming from natural gas and renewable electric generation, and less from coal-fired power plants. However, some issues still remain unresolved with the potential implementation of the CPP.

Some observers say that EPA's CPP essentially proposes an environmental dispatch regime for power plant operation which could potentially result in increased electricity prices to consumers, depending on the generation resource mix employed. But EPA believes adoption of greater energy efficiency measures will actually reduce average retail electricity bills. Compliance may require more natural gas consumption to firm up variable renewable electric generation. Increasing the use of natural gas for power generation has resulted in some concerns, as deliverability and price volatility issues have emerged as recently as this past winter. Power companies, gas suppliers, and regulatory regimes are working on resolving these issues.

The electric utility industry values diversity in fuel choice options since reliance on one fuel or technology can leave electricity producers vulnerable to price and supply volatility. Also, state-specific compliance plans geared to individual state needs may complicate the coordination necessary for reliability purposes. But EPA expects coal to remain a substantial part of the U.S. energy mix through 2030, allowing goals of fuel diversity and generating resource mix to be maintained.

Many fossil-fueled power plants do more than just generate electricity. Some of the power plants scheduled for retirement provide ancillary services to the grid such as voltage support and frequency regulation. Additional retirements of coal-fired capacity resulting from implementing the proposal could impact reserve margins and even grid reliability during weather-related outages or periods of temperature extremes. Incidents of more extreme weather appear to be occurring, and will need to be planned for when considering the types of future generation which may be needed to assure electric system reliability.

Implementing compliance plans will not come without real costs or hard choices for the states and electric utilities that will have to work together. Potential implications for reliability and the ultimate financial costs of the CPP are not known but will become clearer as state compliance plans are filed, and implementation plans become known.

Chapter 2 - On June 18, 2014, the Environmental Protection Agency (EPA) published a proposed rulemaking that would establish guidelines for states to use when developing plans that address carbon dioxide (CO_2) emissions from existing fossil fuel-fired electric generating units. The proposal creates CO_2 emission rate goals—measured in pounds of CO_2 emissions per megawatts-hours (MWh) of electricity generation—for each state to achieve by 2030 and an interim goal to be achieved "on average" between 2020 and 2029. EPA estimates that if the states achieve their individual emission rate goals in 2030, the CO_2 emissions from the electric power sector in the United States would be reduced by 30% compared to 2005 levels.

This report discusses the methodology EPA used to establish state-specific CO_2 emission rate goals that apply to states' overall electricity generation portfolio.

The emission rate goals do not apply directly to individual emission sources. EPA established the emission rate goals by first determining each state's 2012 emission rate baseline, which is generally a function of each state's portfolio of electricity generation in 2012. The resulting baselines in each state vary considerably, reflecting, among other things, the different energy sources used to generate electricity in each state.

To establish the emission rate goals, EPA applied four "building blocks" to the state baselines. The four building blocks involve estimates of various opportunities for states to decrease their emission rates:

- Building block 1: coal-fired power plant efficiency improvements;
- Building block 2: natural gas combined cycle displacement (NGCC) of more carbon-intensive sources, particularly coal;
- Building block 3: increased use of renewable energy and preservation of existing and under construction nuclear power; and
- Building block 4: energy efficiency improvements.

Building blocks 1 and 2 directly affect the CO_2 emission rate at affected EGUs by factoring in EGU efficiency improvements and opportunities to switch from high- to low-carbon power generation. In contrast, building blocks 3 and 4 involve so-called "outside the fence" opportunities that do not directly apply to electricity generation at affected EGUs.

The building blocks affect each state's emission rate in different ways, depending on each state's specific circumstances. On average, block 1 has the smallest average impact, decreasing state emission rate goals (compared to 2012 baselines) by a range of 0% to 6%.

Building block 2, on average, lowers rates by 13%, with a range of impacts from 0% to 38% (compared to baseline). The largest rate changes are seen in states that have both coal-fired EGUs and under-utilized NGCC plants. The smallest rate impacts are in states without any NGCC units and states that already have relatively high NGCC utilization rates.

The under construction nuclear component of building block 3 only affects rates in three states, but its rate impacts are considerable. An amount of at-risk nuclear generation was included in the 2012 baseline rates, lowering some state baselines by as much as 7%.

The renewable energy component of block 3, on average, reduces emission rate baselines by 9%, with a range from 2% to 33%. This block has a greater impact in states that use renewable energy (not counting hydroelectric power) to generate a substantial percentage of their total electricity.

Building block 4 reduces rates, on average, by 13%, with a range of impacts between 4% and 37%. This range is a result of several factors, including (1) the contribution of in-state electricity generation that comes from hydroelectric power or nuclear power; and (2) whether the state is a net importer or net exporter of electricity.

The results of applying the four building blocks do not require or predict a particular outcome in a state's electricity generation profile. The emission rates are a function of EPA's specific emission rate methodology. States may choose to meet emission rate goals by focusing on one or more of the building block strategies or through alternative approaches.

Chapter 3 - Taking action to address climate change by reducing U.S. emissions of greenhouse gases (GHGs) is among President Obama's major goals. At an international conference in Copenhagen in 2009, he committed the United States to reducing emissions of greenhouse gases 17% by 2020, as compared to 2005 levels. At the time, 85 other nations also committed to reductions.

Since U.S. GHG emissions peaked in 2007, a variety of factors—some economic, some the effect of government policies at all levels—have brought the United States more than halfway to reaching the 2020 goal. Getting the rest of the way would likely depend, to some degree, on continued GHG emission reductions from electric power plants, which are the largest source of U.S. emissions.

In June 2013, the President released a Climate Action Plan that addressed this and other climate issues. At the same time, he directed the Environmental Protection Agency (EPA) to propose standards for "carbon pollution" (i.e., carbon dioxide, the principal GHG) from existing power plants by June 2014 and to finalize them in June 2015. Under the President's timetable, by June 2016, states would be required to submit to EPA plans to implement the standards.

On June 2, 2014, EPA responded to the first of these directives by releasing the proposed standards.

The proposal relies on authority given EPA by Congress decades ago in Section 111(d) of the Clean Air Act (CAA). This section has been little used— the last use was in 1996—and never interpreted by the courts, so a number of questions have arisen regarding the extent of EPA's authority and the mechanisms of implementation. EPA tends to refer to the regulations as "guideline documents"—although that term is not used in the statute—perhaps to indicate that the section is intended to give primary authority to the states. The proposed guideline document would set interim (2020s averages) and final (2030) emission rate goals for each state based on four "building blocks"—broad categories that describe different reduction measures; in general, however, the policies to be adopted to reach these goals would be determined by the states, not EPA.

EPA faced a number of issues in developing the proposed regulations:

- How large a reduction in emissions would it propose, and by when?
- What year would it choose as the base against which to measure progress?
- How flexible would it make the regulations? Would it adopt a "mass-based" limit on total emissions or a rate-based (e.g., pounds of carbon dioxide per megawatt-hour of electricity) approach?
- What role might allowance systems play in meeting the goals?
- Will compliance be determined only by the actions of power companies (i.e., "inside the fence" actions) or will actions by energy consumers ("outside the fence") be part of compliance strategies?
- Would states and power companies that have already reduced GHG emissions receive credit for doing so? What about states and power generators with high levels of emissions, perhaps

due to heavy reliance on coal-fired power? Would they be required to reduce emissions more than others, less than others, or the same?

- What role would there be for existing programs at the state and regional levels, such as the Regional Greenhouse Gas Initiative (RGGI), and for broader greenhouse gas reduction programs such as those implemented pursuant to California's AB 32?

This report summarizes EPA's proposal and answers many of these questions. In addition to discussing details of the proposed rule, the report addresses a number of questions regarding the reasons EPA is proposing this rule; EPA's authority under Section 111 of the CAA; EPA's previous experience using that authority; the steps the agency must take to finalize the proposed rule; and other background questions.

Chapter 4 - As a direct result of the Environmental Protection Agency's promulgation of an "endangerment finding" for greenhouse gas (GHG) emissions in December 2009, and its subsequent promulgation of GHG emission standards for new motor vehicles in 2010, the agency has proceeded to control GHG emissions from new and modified *stationary* sources as well. Stationary sources, including power plants, refineries, manufacturing facilities, and others account for about 70% of U.S. emissions of greenhouse gases. If the United States is to reduce its total GHG emissions, as President Obama has committed to do, it will be necessary to reduce emissions from these sources.

EPA's 2010 regulations limiting GHG emissions from new cars and light trucks triggered two Clean Air Act (CAA) provisions affecting stationary sources of air pollution. First, since January 2, 2011, new or modified major stationary sources must undergo New Source Review (NSR) with respect to their GHGs in addition to any other pollutants subject to regulation under the CAA that are emitted by the source. This review requires affected sources to install Best Available Control Technology (BACT) to address their GHG emissions. Second, major sources of GHGs (existing and new) must now obtain permits under Title V of the CAA (or have existing permits modified to include their GHG requirements).

EPA shares congressional concerns about the potential scope of these provisions, primarily because a literal reading of the act would have required as many as 6 million stationary sources to obtain permits. To avoid this result, on May 13, 2010, the agency finalized a "Tailoring Rule" that focuses its resources on the largest emitters while deciding over a six-year period what to do about smaller sources.

Beyond these permitting requirements, EPA has begun the process of establishing emission standards for large stationary sources of GHGs under the act. Thus far, the agency has focused on electric generating units (EGUs), which account for about one-third of total U.S. GHG emissions. The agency proposed performance (emission) standards for new EGUs on January 8, 2014. Guidelines for existing EGUs are to be proposed by June 1.

Many in Congress have suggested that EPA should delay taking action on any stationary sources or should be prevented from doing so. There were at least 10 bills introduced in the 112th Congress that would have delayed or prevented EPA actions on greenhouse gas emissions, and legislation continues to be considered in the 113th. Among the bills introduced, recent attention has focused on H.R. 3826 and S.J.Res. 30. The former, which was ordered reported by the Energy and Commerce Committee, January 28, 2014, would prohibit EPA from promulgating or implementing GHG emission standards for fossil-fueled EGUs until certain stringent requirements were met, and would require that Congress enact new legislation setting an effective date before such standards could be implemented. The latter, a resolution of disapproval under the Congressional Review Act, would render EPA's proposed standards of no force or effect.

This report discusses elements of the GHG controversy, providing background on stationary sources of GHG pollution and identifying options Congress has at its disposal to address GHG issues, including (1) resolutions of disapproval under the Congressional Review Act; (2) freestanding legislation; (3) the use of appropriations bills as a vehicle to influence EPA activity; and (4) amendments to the Clean Air Act, including legislation to establish a new GHG control regime.

Chapter 5 - On June 2, 2014, the U.S. Environmental Protection Agency, under President Obama's Climate Action Plan, proposed a commonsense plan to cut carbon pollution from power plants. The science shows that climate change is already posing risks to our health and our economy. The Clean Power Plan will maintain an affordable, reliable energy system, while cutting pollution and protecting our health and environment now and for future generations.

In: EPA's Proposed Carbon Dioxide Rule ...   ISBN: 978-1-63463-178-5
Editor: Carmella Ramos   © 2014 Nova Science Publishers, Inc.

Chapter 1

EPA'S PROPOSED GREENHOUSE GAS REGULATIONS:IMPLICATIONS FOR THE ELECTRIC POWER SECTOR*

Richard J. Campbell

SUMMARY

The Environmental Protection Agency (EPA) has proposed regulations to reduce greenhouse gas (GHG) emissions from existing power plants. EPA believes that its proposed Clean Power Plan (CPP) will "protect public health, move the United States towards a cleaner environment, and fight climate change while supplying Americans with reliable and affordable power." Burning fossil fuels to produce electricity results in the release of carbon dioxide, and represents the largest source of GHG emissions in the United States. Under its proposed plan, EPA believes it will be possible to lower the carbon intensity of power generation in the United States by approximately 30% in 2030 from carbon dioxide emissions levels in 2005. To achieve this goal, EPA is giving each state a numerical carbon reduction target, based on the state's existing power generation portfolio.

Under the Clean Air Act (CAA) section 111(d), the EPA must identify the best system of emission reductions (BSER) that is adequately

---

* This is an edited, reformatted and augmented version of a Congressional Research Service publication R43621, prepared for Members and Committees of Congress, dated June 23, 2014.

demonstrated and available to reduce pollution. The regulations allow EPA to set goals, and give states the responsibility for creating compliance plans which meet those goals. EPA set the state-specific goals based on (1) measures which improve the efficiency of fossil-fueled power plants, (2) use of lower-emitting generation sources such as natural gas or fuel-switching to natural gas, and use of nuclear power, (3) demand-side efficiency, and (4) renewable electric generation. EPA has suggested these measures as four BSER "building blocks" or options for states to consider when choosing how to meet their specific GHG reduction goals. Under the proposed plan, however, states would have the flexibility to choose the most cost-effective strategies to meet the targets.

EPA's proposal for GHG reduction answers some questions from the electric power sector with regard to the timeframe, timeline, and choices that would be made available for compliance. The CPP proposal sets out a vision for a greater proportion of electricity coming from natural gas and renewable electric generation, and less from coal-fired power plants. However, some issues still remain unresolved with the potential implementation of the CPP.

Some observers say that EPA's CPP essentially proposes an environmental dispatch regime for power plant operation which could potentially result in increased electricity prices to consumers, depending on the generation resource mix employed. But EPA believes adoption of greater energy efficiency measures will actually reduce average retail electricity bills. Compliance may require more natural gas consumption to firm up variable renewable electric generation. Increasing the use of natural gas for power generation has resulted in some concerns, as deliverability and price volatility issues have emerged as recently as this past winter. Power companies, gas suppliers, and regulatory regimes are working on resolving these issues.

The electric utility industry values diversity in fuel choice options since reliance on one fuel or technology can leave electricity producers vulnerable to price and supply volatility. Also, state-specific compliance plans geared to individual state needs may complicate the coordination necessary for reliability purposes. But EPA expects coal to remain a substantial part of the U.S. energy mix through 2030, allowing goals of fuel diversity and generating resource mix to be maintained.

Many fossil-fueled power plants do more than just generate electricity. Some of the power plants scheduled for retirement provide ancillary services to the grid such as voltage support and frequency regulation. Additional retirements of coal-fired capacity resulting from implementing the proposal could impact reserve margins and even grid reliability during weather-related outages or periods of temperature extremes. Incidents of more extreme weather appear to be occurring, and will need to be planned for when considering the types of future generation which may be needed to assure electric system reliability.

Implementing compliance plans will not come without real costs or hard choices for the states and electric utilities that will have to work together. Potential implications for reliability and the ultimate financial costs of the CPP are not known but will become clearer as state compliance plans are filed, and implementation plans become known.

INTRODUCTION

The Environmental Protection Agency (EPA) has proposed regulations to reduce greenhouse gas[1] (GHG) emissions from existing power plants (also referred to as electric generating units or EGUs by EPA). EPA believes that its proposed Clean Power Plan (CPP)[2] will "protect public health, move the United States towards a cleaner environment, and fight climate change while supplying Americans with reliable and affordable power."[3] Carbon emissions are linked by many to anthropogenic climate change,[4] and the EPA cites the Obama Administration's intent to address climate change[5] concerns in its proposed Clean Power Plan to reduce carbon emissions.

Since carbon dioxide (CO_2) from fossil fuel combustion is the primary GHG, and fossil fuels are used for the majority of electric power generation, the focus of the proposed policies is on reducing carbon emissions from power plants. Under its proposed plan, EPA believes it will be possible to lower the CO_2 emissions from power generation in the United States by approximately 30% by 2030 compared to levels in 2005. To achieve this goal, EPA is giving each state a numerical carbon reduction target, based on the state's existing power generation portfolio, and EPA's estimate of the state's potential to reduce power demand.

EPA's guidelines allow a 120-day comment period on the proposal, and require states to file a compliance plan by June 2016. States that choose to join a regional carbon reduction plan would have until June 2018 to submit the plan. The compliance mechanism would require states to reduce the carbon emissions rate of power plants (i.e., overall tons of carbon dioxide emitted per each MegaWatt-hour (MWh) of electricity produced). Whether working individually or regionally, states would be allowed to choose an appropriate mix of generation using diverse fuels (including renewable electricity[6] and nuclear power), energy efficiency, and demand-side management to meet the goals and their own needs.[7]

This report presents an analysis of EPA's proposed plan. Electric utilities and other stakeholders will be analyzing the CPP to understand its provisions, and have until the close of the comment period[8] to provide input. It is possible that the CPP will be modified in response to relevant comments received. The implications of implementing a final CPP are thus unlikely to be known until after the states file their compliance plans which are due by June 2016.

The issues for Congress will be focused on the implications of the CPP on electric power system reliability, the costs of electric power to customers, and the future structure of the electric utility industry which could result from implementation of compliance plans.

BACKGROUND

Burning fossil fuels to produce electricity results in the release of carbon dioxide, and represents the largest source of GHG emissions in the United States. As shown in *Figure 1*, fossil fuel combustion was responsible for approximately 68% of electric power generation as of 2012. Coal was the fuel most used. Coal is also the fossil fuel which emits the most carbon dioxide per unit of electric power produced, averaging 216 pounds of carbon dioxide per million British thermal units (mmBTUs) of energy produced. By comparison, natural gas combustion releases about half the carbon emissions at 117 pounds of carbon dioxide per mmBTU of energy produced.[9]

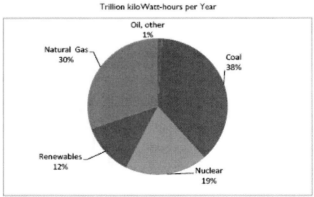

Source: DOE, Annual Energy Outlook, 2014 Early Release, December 16, 2013, http://www.eia.gov/forecasts/ aeo/er/early_elecgen.cfm.

Notes: Renewable electricity includes hydropower, wind, solar, and biomass power generation. "Other" includes other liquid fuels.

Figure 1. U.S. Electricity Generation by Fuel, 2012.

In a 2007 decision, the Supreme Court found in *Massachusetts vs. EPA*[10] that GHG emissions were air pollutants which could be regulated under the Clean Air Act (CAA).[11] EPA then moved in 2009 to declare that GHGs were a threat to public health in its "endangerment" finding, which served as a basis for its subsequent actions.[12] With regard to stationary sources of GHGs, EPA proposed standards in September 2013 for the control of carbon dioxide emissions from new electric power plants burning fossil fuels, under CAA section 111(b) regulations.

EPA has now released a proposal for reducing carbon dioxide emissions from existing power plants which burn fossil fuels. Under CAA 111(d), the EPA must establish a procedure under which states will submit plans establishing standards of performance for existing fossil fuel-fired power plants. The standards of performance are to reflect the degree of emissions limitation achievable through the application of the best system of emission reductions (BSER) that is adequately demonstrated and available to reduce pollution. The regulation under CAA 111(d) allows EPA to set goals, and gives states the responsibility for creating compliance plans which meet EPA's guidelines.

EPA's PROPOSED PLAN FOR EXISTING COAL PLANTS[13]

Under the provisions of EPA's proposed Clean Power Plan, all existing fossil fuel-fired electric power generation plants must comply with new state-specific targets to reduce carbon emissions.[14] The combined state targets are expected to result in reducing carbon emissions from U.S. power generation approximately 30% by 2030 compared to carbon emissions levels in 2005.

EPA has designated four "building blocks" that it used to develop the state-specific GHG reduction goals:

1. *Improve the heat rate[15] of fossil-fueled power plants.* EPA suggests increasing power plant efficiency by equipment upgrades and improvements. Using less fossil fuel to create the same amount of electricity reduces carbon emissions. An average heat rate improvement of 6% is targeted for coal-fired power plants.[16]
2. *Increase use of low-emitting power sources.* EPA suggests more frequent use of power plants with lower carbon emissions resulting in less carbon pollution. Dispatching (i.e., scheduling the operation) of

higher efficiency natural gas combined cycle units more often is
suggested.

3. *Use of more zero -emitting power sources.* EPA suggests expanding
   renewable electricity generation (such as zero-carbon emission wind
   and solar facilities), and nuclear power plants as a way to lower
   carbon emissions.

4. *Using electricity more efficiently.* EPA suggests energy efficiency as a
   way to reduce power demand, with a targeted increase in demand-side
   energy efficiency of 1.5% annually.

EPA recognizes that such options are already being used by some states to
promote clean energy and efficiency goals. EPA considers a BSER to include
measures which improve the efficiency of fossil-fueled power plants, use
lower emitting generation sources such as natural gas or fuel-switching to
natural gas, and use nuclear power and renewable electric generation. Under
the proposed plan, EPA believes the states have the flexibility to choose the
most cost-effective strategies to meet the targets.

States must file a plan by 2016 to comply with EPA's state-specific goals,
unless they choose to join a multi-state regional plan. Each state has been
given a unique carbon emissions reduction goal,[17] which EPA maintains offers
broad flexibility in which to plan and achieve reductions in carbon emissions.
Option 1 would involve a higher level of deployment of the four building
blocks over a longer timeframe (i.e., over 15 years to 2030). EPA also
suggested an alternative path on which it is asking for comment in *Option 2*,
which would allow a lower level of deployment of the four building blocks but
over a shorter timeframe (i.e., over ten years to 2025). EPA has set interim and
final goals for the state-specific goals under both compliance scenarios. They
can meet the goals as individual states, or join together for regional solutions.

The state goals are given as an overall rate of carbon dioxide emissions
intensity, that is, the amount of carbon dioxide emissions in pounds (lbs.) from
fossil-fueled power plants *divided* by the amount of electricity generated in the
state (from fossil-fired generation and low- or zero-carbon emitting power
sources) in MWh. EPA estimates that the state-specific carbon reduction goals
will result in the elimination of approximately 730 million metric tonnes[18] of
carbon by 2030, resulting in a reduction of approximately 30% of carbon levels
compared to 2005.[19]

DISCUSSION OF EPA'S PROPOSAL

Electric power generation in the United States differs regionally, and largely reflects local resources, fuel costs, and availability of fuel supplies.[20] EPA recognizes that it will take time to implement compliance solutions to meet its proposed carbon pollution reduction plan. EPA has attempted to provide flexibility for state compliance with its plan for reducing carbon emissions from existing fossil-fueled power plants.

> The EPA is also proposing to give states considerable flexibility with respect to the timeframes for plan development and implementation, with up to two or three years permitted for final plans to be submitted after the proposed GHG emission guidelines are finalized, and up to fifteen years for all emission reduction measures to be fully implemented.[21]

While 2005 has been mentioned in broader U.S. policy terms for reductions in GHG emissions to 2030, it is not the year that EPA has used in its emissions reduction calculation. EPA chose 2012 as the year from which to establish a baseline for emissions reduction since that was the year for which it has the most complete state emissions, net generation, and capacity data for all affected EGUs.

> For purposes of establishing state goals, historical (2012) electric generation data are used to apply each building block and develop each state's goal (expressed as an adjusted CO2 emission rate in lbs per MWh).[22]

Many regard this as beneficial for many states since U.S. GHG emissions overall have dropped 15% between 2005 and 2012.[23]

Existing State Clean Energy Programs

EPA also considers expanding state renewable electric programs and portfolio standards as tools to reduce GHG emissions. However, for purposes of establishing a baseline, existing hydropower is not included.

> Hydropower generation is excluded from this existing 2012 generation for purposes of quantifying BSER-related [renewable

electricity] generation potential because building the methodology from a baseline that includes large amounts of existing hydropower generation could distort regional targets that are later applied to states lacking that existing hydropower capacity. The exclusion of pre-existing hydropower generation from the baseline of this target-setting framework does not prevent states from considering incremental hydropower generation from existing facilities (or later-built facilities) as an option for compliance with state goals.[24]

However, states will not receive credit for "early action" taken to reduce GHGs in the period prior to the timeframe of the proposal. Therefore, GHG reductions resulting from state renewable portfolio standards (and other similar measures) in the period from 2005 to 2012 will not count towards GHG reductions in the 2020 to 2030 timeframe. But since they are programs already in place, EPA considers these programs as helpful to meeting state-specific goals in the compliance timeframe.

The EPA is also proposing that measures a state takes after the date of this proposal, or programs already in place, which result in CO_2 emissions reduction during the 2020-2030 period, would apply toward achievement of the state's 2030 CO_2 emissions goal. Thus, states with currently existing programs and policies, and states that put in new programs and policies early, will be better positioned to achieve the goals.[25]

While states must begin compliance with the proposed plan by 2020, full compliance is not required until 2030. EPA points out that its four building blocks are suggested as a framework for implementation; the states themselves will decide how to meet their goals. EPA also suggests that regional compliance strategies would be acceptable under its proposal.

Each state will have the flexibility to design a program to meet its goal in a manner that reflects its particular circumstances and energy and environmental policy objectives. Each state can do so alone or can collaborate with other states on multi-state plans that may provide additional opportunities for cost savings and flexibility.[26]

In establishing the state-specific goals for GHG reduction, EPA believes it has taken into consideration the regional differences that exist in power generation types and resources. Each state's goal reflects the fact that a state's

CO_2 emissions are a result of how efficiently its fossil-fueled power plants operate, and how much they operate. Under the state-specific goals, the highest allowed rate of GHG emissions is 1,783 lbs. of CO_2 per MWh of electricity produced for North Dakota, while the lowest emissions rate is 215 lbs. of CO_2 per MWh in Washington state,[27] with the apparent disparity in state goals reflecting the existing underlying generation mix in the states.

Best System of Emissions Reduction

EPA has modeled the opportunities for heat rate improvement, dispatch of more gas and less coal, increased renewable and nuclear generation, and end-use energy efficiency. The agency considers these actions representing the "Best System of Emissions Reductions" which is adequately demonstrated.[28]

Overall, the BSER proposed here is based on a range of measures that fall into four main categories, or "building blocks," which comprise improved operations at EGUs, dispatching lower-emitting EGUs, and zero-emitting energy sources, and end-use energy efficiency. All of these measures have been amply demonstrated via their current widespread use by utilities and states.

The proposed guidelines are structured so that states would not be required to use each and every one of the measures that the EPA determines constitute the BSER or to apply any one of those measures to the same extent that the EPA determines is achievable at reasonable cost. Instead, in developing its plan, each state will have the flexibility to select the measure or combination of measures it prefers in order to achieve its CO_2 emission reduction goal.[29]

As part of the BSER determination, the EPA considered the impacts that implementation of the emission reductions [based on the combination of the blocks] would have on the cost of electricity and electricity system reliability.... Importantly, the proposed BSER, expressed as a numeric goal for each state, provides states with the flexibility to determine how to achieve the reductions (i.e., greater reductions from one building block and less from another) and to adjust the timing in which reductions are achieved, in order to address key issues such as cost to consumers, electricity system reliability and the remaining useful life of existing generation assets.[30]

The EPA is proposing to evaluate and approve state plans based on four general criteria: 1) enforceable measures that reduce EGU CO2 emissions; 2) projected achievement of emission performance equivalent to the goals established by the EPA, on a timeline equivalent to that in the emission guidelines; 3) quantifiable and verifiable emission reductions; and 4) a process for biennial reporting on plan implementation, progress toward achieving CO2 goals, and implementation of corrective actions, if necessary.[31]

In devising a compliance strategy, EPA proposes to allow each state to design a GHG reduction program using strategies or technologies the state selects.

> To meet its goal, each state will be able to design programs that use the measures it selects, and these may include the combination of building blocks most relevant to its specific circumstances and policy preferences. States may also identify technologies or strategies that are not explicitly mentioned in any of the four building blocks and may use those technologies or strategies as part of their overall plans (e.g., market-based trading programs or construction of new natural combined cycle units or nuclear plants).[32]

EPA believes that shifting electric power production from coal-fired power plants to natural gas combined-cycle generation (NGCC) represents a major opportunity to reduce GHG emissions due to the greater overall efficiency of the newer NGCC generation fleet especially as compared to older coal-fired power plants, and the current underutilization of NGCC generation capacity.

> Our analysis indicated that the potential CO2 reductions available through re-dispatch from steam EGUs to NGCC units are substantial. As of 2012, there was approximately 245 GW of NGCC capacity in the United States, 196 GW of which was placed in service between 2000 and 2012. In 2012, the average utilization rate of U.S. NGCC capacity was 46 percent, well below the utilization rates the units are capable of achieving. In 2012, approximately 10 percent of NGCC plants operated at annual utilization rates of 70 percent or higher, and 19 percent of NGCC units operated at utilization rates of at least 70 percent over the summer season. Average reported availability generally exceeds 85 percent. We recognize that the ability to increase NGCC utilization rates may also be affected by infrastructure and system considerations, such as limits on the ability of the natural gas industry to produce and deliver the increased

quantities of natural gas, the ability of steam EGUs to reduce generation while remaining ready to supply electricity when needed in peak demand hours, and the ability of the electric transmission system to accommodate the changed geographic pattern of generation.[33]

The amount of re-dispatch from coal-fired EGUs to NGCC units that takes place as a result of this competition is highly relevant to overall power sector GHG emissions, because a typical NGCC unit produces less than half as much CO_2 per MWh of electricity generated as a typical coal-fired EGU.[34]

Under its proposal, EPA has suggested a range of equipment upgrades and improvement options to increase heat rates (specifically at existing coal-fired power plants), which it believes represents cost-effective opportunities to reduce GHG emissions.

Our assessment of heat rate improvements showed that these measures would achieve CO_2 emission reductions at low costs, although compared to other measures, the available reductions were relatively limited in quantity. Specifically, our analysis indicated that average CO_2 emission reductions of 1.3 to 6.7 percent could be achieved by coal-fired steam EGUs through adoption of best practices, and that additional average reductions of up to four percent could be achieved through equipment upgrades. Heat rate improvements pay for themselves at least in part through reductions in fuel costs, generally making this a relatively inexpensive approach for reducing CO_2 emissions. We estimated that CO_2 reductions of between four and six percent from overall heat rate improvements could be achieved on average across the nation's fleet of coal-fired steam EGUs for net costs in a range of $6 to $12 per metric ton.[35]

Although heat rate improvements have the potential to reduce CO_2 emissions from all types of affected EGUs, the EPA's analysis indicates the potential is significantly greater for coal-fired steam EGUs than for other EGUs, and for purposes of determining the best system of emission reduction at this time EPA is conservatively proposing to base its estimate of CO_2 emission reductions from heat rate improvements on coal-fired steam EGUs only.[36]

Fuel Switching

EPA sees the opportunity for coal to natural gas conversions at existing power plants (rather than co-firing coal and natural gas together) as having a great potential to reduce GHGs. While converting a coal-fired power plant to natural gas would be considered a higher cost option compared to other heat rate improvements, EPA believes the incremental difference in the cost of fuel would be the most significant cost component.

> Natural gas co-firing or conversion at coal-fired steam EGUs offers greater potential CO_2 emission reductions than heat rate improvements, but at a higher cost (although less than the cost of applying CCS [Carbon Capture and Storage] technology). Because natural gas contains less carbon than an energy-equivalent quantity of coal, converting a coal-fired steam EGU to burn only natural gas would reduce the unit's CO_2 emissions by approximately 40 percent. The CO_2 reductions are generally proportional to the amount of gas substituted for coal, so if an EGU continued to burn mostly coal while co-firing natural gas as, for example, 10 percent of the EGU's total heat input, the CO_2 emission reductions would be approximately four percent. The EPA determined that the most significant cost associated with natural gas conversion or co-firing is likely to be the incremental cost of natural gas relative to the cost of coal. [37]

Nuclear Power

Another higher cost option would be the construction of new nuclear power plants. However, EPA views the completion of nuclear units currently under construction, and avoiding the "premature" retirement of an estimated 6% of existing nuclear capacity, to be important to GHG reduction goals in some states.[38]

> Policies that encourage development of renewable energy capacity and discourage premature retirement of nuclear capacity could be useful elements of CO_2 reduction strategies and are consistent with current industry behavior. Costs of CO_2 reductions achievable through these policies have been estimated in a range from $10 to $40 per metric ton.[39]
>
> Nuclear generating capacity facilitates CO_2 emission reductions at fossil fuel-fired EGUs by providing carbon-free generation that can

replace generation at those EGUs. Because of their relatively low variable operating costs, nuclear EGUs that are available to operate typically are dispatched before fossil fuel-fired EGUs. Increasing the amount of nuclear capacity relative to the amount that would otherwise be available to operate is therefore a technically viable approach to support reducing CO_2 emissions from affected fossil fuel-fired EGUs.[40]

We have determined that, based on available information regarding the cost and performance of the nuclear fleet, preserving the operation of at-risk nuclear capacity would likely be capable of achieving CO_2 reductions from affected EGUs at a reasonable cost.[41]

In addition to the nuclear generation taken into account in the state goals analysis, any additional new nuclear generating units or uprating of existing nuclear units, relative to a baseline of capacity as of the date of proposal of the emission guidelines, could be a component of state plans.[42]

Demand-Side Energy Efficiency

The fourth building block of the BSER identified by EPA is "cost-effective" demand-side energy efficiency programs.

The purposes of demand-side energy efficiency programs vary; goals include to reduce GHG emissions by reducing fossil-fired generation, help states achieve energy savings goals, save energy and money for consumers and improve electricity reliability. They are typically funded through a small fee or surcharge on customer electricity bills, but can also be funded by other sources, such as from CO2 [allowance auction program] proceeds. [43]

California has been advancing energy efficiency through utility-run demand-side energy efficiency programs for decades and considers energy efficiency "the bedrock upon which climate policies are built." It requires its investor-owned utilities to meet electricity load "through all available energy efficiency and demand reduction resources that are cost-effective, reliable and feasible."[44]

Demand-side energy efficiency programs produce electricity-dependent services with less electricity, and thereby support reduced generation from existing fossil fuel-fired EGUs by reducing the demand for that generation. Reduced generation results in lower CO2 emissions. More than 40 states already have established some form of demand-side energy efficiency polices, and individual states have avoided up to 13 percent of their electricity demand.[45]

New Source Review

The New Source Review[46] (NSR) program was designed to prevent the degradation of air quality from the construction of new facilities or modification of existing facilities which have potentially harmful emissions. Efficiency improvements to power plants that reduce regulated pollutants should not theoretically trigger NSR requirements, unless the improvements result in an increase in emissions (e.g., because the modified plant operates for more hours). EPA has proposed that states be given a primary role with regard to NSR determinations.

> As part of its CAA section 111(d) plan, a state may impose requirements that require an affected EGU to undertake a physical or operational change to improve the unit's efficiency that results in an increase in the unit's dispatch and an increase in the unit's annual emissions. If the emissions increase associated with the unit's changes exceeds the thresholds in the NSR regulations discussed above for one or more regulated NSR pollutants, including the netting analysis, the changes would trigger NSR.
>
> While there may be instances in which an NSR permit would be required, we expect those situations to be few. As previously discussed in this preamble, states have considerable flexibility in selecting varied measures as they develop their plans to meet the goals of the emissions guidelines. One of these flexibilities is the ability of the state to establish the standards of performance in their CAA section 111(d) plans in such a way so that their affected sources, in complying with those standards, in fact would not have emissions increases that trigger NSR. To achieve this, the state would need to conduct an analysis consistent with the NSR regulatory requirements that supports its determination that as long as affected sources comply with the standards of performance in their CAA section 111(d) plan, the source's emissions would not increase in a way that trigger NSR requirements. [47]
>
> The EPA is aware of the potential for "rebound effects" from improvements in heat rates at individual EGUs. In this context, a rebound effect would occur where, because of an improvement in its heat rate, an EGU experiences a reduction in variable operating costs that makes the

EGU more competitive relative to other EGUs and consequently raises the EGU's generation output. The increase in the EGU's CO2 emissions associated with the increase in generation output would offset the reduction in the EGU's CO2 emissions caused by the decrease in its heat rate and rate of CO2 emissions per unit of generation output. The extent of the offset would depend on the extent to which the EGU's generation output increased (as well as the CO2 emission rates of the EGUs whose generation was displaced). The EPA considers the rebound effect to be a potential concern if heat rate improvements were the only approaches being considered for the BSER, but believes that the effect can be addressed by establishing the BSER as a combination of approaches that includes not only heat rate improvements but also approaches that will encourage reductions in electricity demand or increases in generation from lower- or zero-emitting EGUs.[48]

ISSUES RELATED TO COMPLIANCE STRATEGIES

The EPA's proposal for GHG reduction answers questions from the electric power sector with regard to the timeframe, timeline, and choices that would be made available for compliance. The CPP proposal sets out a vision for a greater proportion of electricity coming from natural gas and renewable electric generation, and less from coal-fired power plants, with state-specific goals for carbon emissions reductions proposed for 2030. However, there are still some unresolved issues remaining with potential implementation of the CPP.

Potential Impacts on Retail Electricity Prices

Under the Energy Policy Act of 2005 (P.L. 109-58), security constrained economic dispatch is defined in section 1234 as follows:

> ... the operation of generation facilities to produce energy at the lowest cost to reliably serve consumers, recognizing any operational limits of generation and transmission facilities.

EPA's CPP recognizes that security constrained economic dispatch "assures reliable and affordable electricity."[49] However, some observers say that EPA's CPP essentially proposes an environmental dispatch regime for power plant operation.[50] Under environmental dispatch, the goal is to use "cleaner" power generating units (i.e., which emit the least pollutants) by scheduling these plants to operate first and as much as possible to serve load demands.

Power plants today are generally scheduled to operate (i.e., dispatched) under an economic dispatch regime whereby power generation units are dispatched using generating units with the lowest costs. Thus, under these economic dispatch regimes, the cost of power generation is characterized by a power plant's efficiency or heat rate, its variable costs of generation, its variable costs of environmental compliance, and its start-up costs.[51]

The increased availability of natural gas has resulted in lower prices for wholesale electricity, with a general expectation that wholesale prices will remain relatively low for the next few years.[52] EPA has conceded that this increased demand could push natural gas prices higher.[53]

There is a concern that shifting to an environmental dispatch regime could potentially result in increased electricity prices to consumers, depending on the generation resource mix employed. However, EPA expects only a "modest impact" on retail prices will result.

> As described below in Section X, the results indicate that the proposed state goals (discussed in Section VII) are readily achievable with no adverse impacts on electricity system reliability, and that impacts on retail electricity prices are modest and fall within the range of price variability seen historically in response to changes in factors such as weather and fuel supply.[54]
>
> Retail electricity prices are projected to increase 6 to 7 percent under Option 1 and increase by roughly 4 percent under Option 2, both in 2020 and on an average basis across the contiguous U.S. By 2030 under Option 1, electricity prices are projected to increase by about 3 percent.[55]

Moreover, EPA expects that energy efficiency measures may lead to an actual reduction in the average retail bill for electricity of 9% by 2030.

> Average monthly electricity bills are anticipated to increase by roughly 3 percent in 2020, but decline by approximately 9 percent by 2030. This is a result of the increasing penetration of demand-side programs that more than offset increased prices to end users by their expected savings from reduced electricity use.[56]

Implications for Fuel Diversity

EPA's CPP proposal ostensibly involves natural gas consumption under two of the four legs of the BSER stool. EPA has suggested shifting the dispatch of power generators to lower-emitting sources by increased scheduling of higher efficiency natural gas combined cycle units. Scheduling these plants will result in higher natural gas consumption.[57] EPA has also suggested using more zero-emitting sources by deploying more renewable generation, which in many parts of the United States will require more natural gas consumption to make variable renewable electric generation more firm (i.e., provide power as renewable electric generation ebbs).

As of 2012, electric power generation used 8.5 trillion cubic feet (TCF) of natural gas.[58] EPA's CPP proposal essentially favors a switch to natural gas as the primary fuel used for power generation, and estimates an increase of 1.2 TCF over 2012 consumption in 2020.[59] However, increasing the use of natural gas for power generation raises some concerns, as deliverability and price volatility issues have emerged as recently as this past winter with the demand spikes associated with the Polar Vortex cold weather events.[60] Recovery of costs from the Polar Vortex have proved to be an issue for some utilities,[61] and the performance of demand response programs in periods of extreme weather (e.g., in the winter especially) have come under question.[62]

FERC is working to improve coordination between the electricity and natural gas industries.[63] Electricity generators get their natural gas from major pipelines or local distribution companies, and these deliveries are usually scheduled during nomination cycles.[64] More cost-effective, natural gas storage facilities may be required for electric power production purposes, if greater natural gas use for power generation is expected. However, the regulatory regime (i.e., Regional Transmission Organization markets or traditional regulation) in place will likely have a bearing on what choices are available to natural gas generators with regard to gas storage options or contracting for firm capacity vs. the "just-in-time" manner of natural gas deliveries traditionally available to power generators.

The electric utility industry values diversity in fuel choice options since reliance on one fuel or technology can leave electricity producers vulnerable to price and supply volatility. EPA's proposal expects additional retirements of coal-fired power plants, with some new NGCC capacity likely built to replace retiring coal capacity. Nuclear power plants are also aging, and some plants expected to be in operation in the 2020 to 2030 timeframe could face premature retirement for a variety of reasons ranging from plant age to electricity market or other conditions.

Unless electricity storage capacity is increased or other concepts develop, natural gas will likely be used to smooth the variable output of some renewable electricity technologies. The developing potential for a heavier reliance on natural gas for power generation is a concern for many in the power sector. EPA, for its part, believes that its BSER proposal can help preserve fuel diversity goals.

> Large vertically integrated utilities generally have options within all four building blocks. They tend to have large and, as a general matter, at least somewhat diverse generation fleets. For their higher-emitting units, they have opportunities to use measures that reduce the units' CO_2 emission rates, such as heat rate improvements, co-firing, or fuel switching. While this proposal preserves fuel diversity, with over 30 percent of projected 2030 generation coming from coal and over 30 percent from natural gas, even companies that have traditionally depended upon coal to supply the majority of their generation are diversifying their fleets, increasing their opportunities for re-dispatch.[65]

Conversion of Coal to Natural Gas Firing

Switching a coal burning plant to natural gas can be a major undertaking as the boiler, fuel handling, and fuel storage areas would have to be modified or replaced. A major engineering study would have to be undertaken to determine the cost and extent of work to be performed for a specific power plant unit. Coal power plants can have multiple units (i.e., with separate steam boilers), some of varying ages and designs. A power plant location near a major natural gas pipeline would make supplying natural gas to the facility easier, although a local natural gas distribution company could also supply the fuel.

Adding a gas turbine to an existing steam turbine would be one option, but not without challenges or significant modifications based on the age of the existing steam turbine and balance of plant. Moderate increases in plant efficiency are possible from such a modification. A conversion to a combined-cycle configuration could be a major modification, both in terms of work performed and cost. But a considerable increase in power output and efficiency could result from such an upgrade.[66]

Regulatory, Policy, and Reliability Concerns

State-specific compliance plans geared to individual state needs may complicate the coordination necessary for reliability purposes. The individual state compliance plans required by EPA's CPP may have to be submitted to multiple jurisdictions (i.e., state public utility commissions, Regional Transmission Organizations, the North American Electric Reliability Corporation, and FERC) at a number of deliberative levels before a compliance plan can be finalized.[67]

Many fossil-fueled power plants do more than just generate electricity. Many power plants provide ancillary services such as voltage support and frequency regulation to the grid. Additional retirements of coal-fired capacity can impact reserve margins, potentially impacting reliability when needed during weather-related outages or periods of temperature extremes.

Incidents of more extreme weather appear to be occurring, and will need to be planned for when considering the types of future generation which may need to be built to assure electric system reliability.[68] EIA currently expects that a total of 60 GigaWatts of coal capacity will retire by 2020, with 90% of these retirements taking place by 2016 "coinciding with the first year of enforcement for the Mercury and Air Toxics Standards."[69] Much of this capacity scheduled for retirement was dispatched during the recent Polar Vortex, adding concern to how the grid will meet power demands in future weather extremes.[70]

EPA's CPP proposal relies on state-implemented renewable portfolio standards (RPSs) and energy efficiency resource standards going forward. However, many state renewable portfolio standards and goals are scheduled to expire in the 2015 to 2020 timeframe, with more by 2025.[71] And many state RPS policies with mandatory requirements have cost caps to ensure that the targets can be met cost-effectively. Similarly, many state energy efficiency resource standards are expiring by 2020.[72]

The transmission system itself is aging and in need of modernization.[73] The grid is stressed in many regions because the system is being used in a manner for which it was not designed. More transmission capacity will likely be needed to handle potentially more transmission transactions under the EPA proposal. Much of the transmission system was built by individual electric utilities to serve their own power plants. New power plants or increased use of existing NGCC capacity may require upgraded transmission facilities, and potentially new natural gas infrastructure to provide fuel. Increased dependence on renewable generation will likely require new transmission lines, and many of today's transmission projects awaiting regulatory approvals are intended to serve renewable electricity projects.

FERC identified public policy requirements (such as state renewable portfolio standards) as drivers which should be elevated to the level of reliability when it comes to approving new transmission projects in its Order No. 1000, *Transmission Planning and Cost Allocation.*[74] Actual implementation of regional compliance plans will demonstrate whether the regime for transmission planning and cost sharing will achieve FERC's goals.

The focus of the EPA's CPP proposal will arguably fall on coal-fired power plants, with at least two of the four building blocks centering on coal plant efficiency, dispatch, and emissions. The age and condition of coal-fired power plants are key considerations in a decision to upgrade or modify plants. Power plants in Regional Transmission Organization (RTO) regions operate in competitive environments where a power plant's operating and maintenance costs are not guaranteed recovery. The additional costs of plant upgrades may not be cost-effective under RTO electricity market regimes or prices. State implementation plans for EPA's CPP may also result in differing requirements within RTO regions for competitive generators. Capacity markets designed to incentivize the construction of new generation in regions with competitive markets have had mixed results. New power plants will most likely be built in regions of the country with traditional regulation using tools like integrated resource planning, and rules allowing cost recovery from ratepayers for approved investments.[75]

Potential for Varying State Impacts

EPA's state-specific GHG emissions goals vary considerably in magnitude, leading to concerns that some states may have much more to do than others and thus compliance with the CPP could result in "winners and losers." The approach to compliance taken by each state will certainly have a unique cost and economic impact, and these could vary considerably between states. However, EPA asserts the benefits of GHG reduction will far outweigh these costs. The agency says that the state-specific goals reflect each state's unique emissions profile and generation resource mix, and maintains that the flexibility offered by its "building blocks" approach will allow states the opportunity to choose a strategy capable of minimizing compliance costs and economic impacts.

Similarly, we recognize and appreciate that states operate with differing circumstances and policy preferences. For example, states have differing access to specific fuel types, and the variety of types of EGUs operating in different states is broad and significant. States are part of assorted EGU dispatch systems and vary in the amounts of electricity that they import and export. For these reasons, we also recognize and appreciate the value in allowing and promoting multi-state reduction strategies.[76]

CONCLUSION

Moving forward, EPA GHG regulations can provide a basis for the evolution of the U.S. Electric Power Sector. EPA recognizes that the grid and many of its fossil-fueled power plants are aging, and provides input via the CPP as to how a future national system providing cleaner energy choices could be powered. EPA believes the benefits of a cleaner environment from its plan are without question. However, meeting the goals of EPA's proposed plan will effectively require less power generation from coal-fired power plants, or even outright retirements of coal-fired generation. Considering the average age of the coal-fired power plant fleet, more retirements are likely when the costs of efficiency improvements or upgrades are weighed in compliance plans.

EPA is not proposing the adoption of any new technologies, but suggests a framework for transition. Implementing compliance plans will not come without real costs or making hard choices for the states and electric utilities who will have to work together to find an acceptable compromise. The potential implications for reliability, and the ultimate financial costs of the CPP will become clearer as state compliance plans are filed, and implementation plans become known.

End Notes

[1] Greenhouse gases, according to EPA, are any gases that absorb infrared radiation in the atmosphere. There are six greenhouse gases addressed by EPA regulatory actions: carbon dioxide (CO2), methane (CH4), nitrous oxide (N2O), and fluorinated gases—sulfur hexafluoride (SF6), hydrofluorocarbons (HFCs), and perfluorocarbons (PFCs). Carbon dioxide is the most prevalent GHG produced by combustion of fossil fuels. See http://www.epa.gov/climatechange/ ghgemissions/gases.html.

[2] See EPA's proposed Clean Power Plan at http://www2.epa.gov/sites/production/files/2014-05/documents/ 20140602proposal-cleanpowerplan.pdf. (CPP)

[3] Environmental Protection Agency, "EPA Proposes First Guidelines to Cut Carbon Pollution from Existing Power Plants/Clean Power Plan is flexible proposal to ensure a healthier environment, spur innovation and strengthen the economy," press release, June 2, 2014, http://www2.epa.gov/carbon-pollution-standards/clean-power-plan-proposedrule.

[4] "Humans tap the huge pool of fossil carbon for energy, and affect the global carbon cycle by transferring fossil carbon—which took millions of years to accumulate underground—into the atmosphere over a relatively short time span. As a result, the atmosphere contains approximately 35% more CO_2 today than prior to the beginning of the industrial revolution. As the CO_2 concentration grows it increases the degree to which the atmosphere traps incoming radiation from the sun, which further warms the planet." CRS Report RL34059, The Carbon Cycle: Implications for Climate Change and Congress, by Peter Folger.

[5] Executive Office of the President, The President's Climate Action Plan, June 2013, http://www.whitehouse.gov/sites/ default/files/image/president27sclimateactionplan.pdf.

[6] Renewable electricity includes power generation from wind, solar, geothermal, and biomass sources. However, while hydropower is generally considered as renewable, some would argue that hydropower from large dams with impoundments have potentially harmful environmental impacts both upstream and downstream from the dam.

[7] EPA says that to date, 47 states have demand-side efficiency programs, 38 have renewable portfolio standards or goals, and 10 states have market-based greenhouse gas emissions programs.

[8] Comments on the proposed rule must be received on or before October 16, 2014.

[9] Energy Information Administration, "How Much Carbon Dioxide Is Produced When Different Fuels Are Burned?," June 4, 2014, http://www.eia.gov/tools/faqs/faq.cfm?id=73&t=11.

[10] 549 U.S. 497, 529 (2007).

[11] 42 U.S.C. 7401 et seq. (as amended).

[12] U.S. Environmental Protection Agency, Endangerment and Cause or Contribute Findings for Greenhouse Gases under Section 202(a) of the Clean Air Act, November 22, 2013, http://www.epa.gov/climatechange/endangerment/.

[13] EPA, Clean Power Plan Proposed Rule, June 2, 2014, http://www2.epa.gov/carbon-pollution-standards/clean-powerplan-proposed-rule.

[14] U.S. Environmental Protection Agency, "Carbon Pollution Emission Guidelines for Existing Stationary Sources: Electric Utility Generating Units," 79 Federal Register 34829, June 18, 2014. (EMEGU)

[15] Heat rate is the efficiency of conversion from fuel energy input to electrical energy output often expressed in terms of BTU per kiloWatt-hour.

[16] A discussion of potential improvements at coal-fired power plants is presented in CRS Report R43343, Increasing the Efficiency of Existing Coal-Fired Power Plants, by Richard J. Campbell.

[17] EMEGU, Table 8, Proposed State Goals.

[18] One tonne (also known as a metric ton) is a unit of mass equaling 1,000 kilograms.

[19] EPA, EPA Fact Sheet—Cutting Carbon Pollution from Power Plants, June 2, 2014, http://www2.epa.gov/sites/production/files/2014-06/documents/20140602fs-important-numbers-clean-power-plan.pdf.

[20] Edison Electric Institute, Different Regions of the Country Use Different Fuel Mixes to Generate Electricity, 2014, http://www.eei.org/issuesandpolicy/generation/fueldiversity/Documents/map_fuel_diversity.pdf.

[21] EMEGU, p. 34940.

[22] EMEGU, p. 34863.

[23] Matthew Philips, "EPA Did the Power Industry a Big Favor by Using 2005 Levels," Bloomberg BusinessWeek, June 2, 2014, http://www.businessweek.com/articles/2014-06-02/epa-did-the-power-industry-a-big-favor-by-using-2005- levels.

[24] EMEGU, p. 34867.

[25] EMEGU, p. 34839.

[26] EMEGU, p. 34833.

[27] EMEGU, Table 8.

[28] EPA, Office of Air and Radiation, Goal Computation Technical Support Document, Technical Support Document for the CAA Section 111(d) Emission Guidelines for Existing Power Plants, June 2014, http://www2.epa.gov/sites/ production/files/2014-05/documents/20140602tsd-goal-computation.pdf.

[29] EMEGU, p. 34835.

[30] EMEGU, p. 34836.

[31] EMEGU, p. 34838.

[32] EMEGU, p. 34837.

[33] EMEGU, p. 34857.

[34] EMEGU, p. 34862.

[35] EMEGU, p. 34856.

[36] EMEGU, p. 34859.

[37] EMEGU, p. 34857.

[38] "EIA in its most recent Annual Energy Outlook has projected an additional 5.7 GW of capacity reductions to the nuclear fleet.... [EPA views] this 5.7 GW, which comprises an approximately six percent share of nuclear capacity, as a reasonable proxy for the amount of nuclear capacity at risk of retirement." EMEGU, p. 34871.

[39] EMEGU, p. 34858.

[40] EMEGU, p. 34870.

[41] EMEGU, p. 34871.

[42] EMEGU, p. 34923.

[43] EMEGU, p. 34849.

[44] EMEGU, p. 34850.

[45] EMEGU, p. 34858.

[46] NSR was established by Congress as part of the 1977 Clean Air Act Amendments (P.L. 95-95), and is codified in sections 165-169 of the act. NSR requires pre-construction permits and the application of Best Available Control Technology at new major sources of air pollution, and at major modifications of existing major sources.

[47] EMEGU, p. 34928.

[48] EMEGU, p. 34859.

[49] EMEGU, p. 34862.

[50] "Scheduling of power plant operation or intertie access in the order of increasing damage to the environment, with the least environmentally damaging first." See http://www.bpa.gov/news/pubs/Pages/Definitions---E.aspx.

[51] FERC Staff, Economic Dispatch: Concepts, Practices and Issues, Federal Energy Regulatory Commission, November 13, 2005, http://www.ferc.gov/eventcalendar/ Files/200511101 72953-FERC%20Staff%20Presentation.pdf.

[52] See EIA, Natural Gas Section, at http://www.eia.gov/forecasts/archive/aeo13/ source_natural_gas_all.cfm#netexporter.

[53] "Under both approaches, the shifting in generation from higher-emitting steam EGUs to lower-emitting NGCC units results in an increase in natural gas production and price. The two-block approach results in a production increase of 19-22 percent and a price increase of 10-11 percent. The four-block approach results in a production increase of 12-14 percent and a price increase of 9-12 percent." EMEGU, p. 34933.

[54] EMEGU, p. 34885.

[55] EMEGU, p. 34935.

[56] EMEGU, p. 34934.

[57] "Given that significant underutilized NGCC exists in various U.S. regions, the possibility of further shifting from coal base load plants to natural gas intermediate capacity exists. A recent study by the Massachusetts Institute of Technology in 2011 noted that the existing U.S. NGCC generation fleet had an average capacity factor of approximately 41%, while its design capacity allowed such plants to operate at 85%. The MIT study looked at a scenario across selected regions of the United States which mimicked the 'full dispatch' of existing natural gas combined cycle plants. The study concluded that under such a scenario (while noting that transmission constraints exist), there is 'sufficient surplus NGCC capacity to displace roughly one-third of U.S. coal generation, reducing CO_2 emissions from the power sector by 20%.'" See CRS Report R42950, Prospects for Coal in Electric Power and Industry, by Richard J. Campbell, Peter Folger, and Phillip Brown. (CoalProspects)

[58] EIA Annual Energy Outlook 2014.

[59] EMEGU, p. 34934.

[60] FERC, 2014Winter 2013-2014 Operations and Market Performance in RTOs and ISOs, AD14-8-000, April 1, 2014, http://www.ferc.gov/legal/staff-reports/2014/04-01-14.pdf.

[61] Veronique Bugnion, The Polar Vortex Wreaks Havoc On Utility Bills, Energy Collective, January 31, 2014, http://theenergycollective.com/vbugnion/334481/polar-vortex-wreaks-havoc-utility-bills.

[62] "Not all events requiring commitment of demand resources will occur during the spring, summer, and early fall, when the Limited and Extended Summer Demand products apply. As the Commission's gas-electric coordination investigation has shown, reliability problems can occur during the winter when gas-fired generators may have difficulty with obtaining natural gas or transportation of natural gas. See Communication of Operational Information Between Natural Gas Pipelines and Electric Transmission Operators, Order No. 787, FERC Stats. & Regs. ¶ 31,350 (cross-referenced at 145 FERC ¶ 61,134, at P 8 (2013)) ("short term swings in demand by gas-fired electric generators resulting from redispatch by electric transmission operators may be difficult to manage, particularly during times of coincident peak loads on interstate natural gas pipelines and electric transmission systems, such as during unusual cold weather events when end-use customers may rely on both natural gas and electricity"). See also PJM supplemental answer at 7 (discussing PJM's need for demand response during the polar vortex on January 7 and 8, 2014, and indicating that all of its demand response was Limited Demand Response and therefore could not be required to run)." See 146 FERC ¶ 61,052, footnote 48.

[63] FERC, Natural Gas—Electric Coordination, June 2014, http://www.ferc.gov/industries/electric/indus-act/electriccoord.asp.

[64] "The natural gas industry generally follows the scheduling cycles adopted by the [North American Energy Standards Board (NAESB)], which FERC regulations incorporate by reference. The NAESB standards set a nationwide natural gas operating day (Gas Day), beginning at 9:00 a.m. CCT [Central Clock Time] and ending at 9:00 a.m. CCT the following day. Current regulations provide for a minimum of four standard nomination

cycles over that 24-hour period with a 'Timely Cycle' and 'Evening Cycle' for nominations closing in the prior day and two 'Intra-Day' nominations during the Gas Day." See http://www.vnf.com/2311.

[65] EMEGU, p. 34886.

[66] See Table 1, "Summary of Emission Reduction Scenarios," Congressional Distribution Memorandum CD145, Summary of Studies on Achieving Increased Coal Power Plant Efficiency and Lower Carbon Dioxide Emissions, January 15, 2014, http://rsinquery .loc.gov/crsx/products-nd/14.5.doc.pdf.

[67] See CoalProspects, "Electricity Reliability—State and Market Inputs."

[68] See CRS Report R42696, Weather-Related Power Outages and Electric System Resiliency, by Richard J. Campbell.

[69] Energy Information Administration, "AEO2014 Projects More Coal-Fired Power Plant Retirements by 2016 Than Have Been Scheduled," February 14, 2014, http://www.eia.gov/ todayinenergy/detail.cfm?id=15031.

[70] Matthew L. Wald, "Coal to the Rescue, but Maybe Not Next Winter," The New York Times, March 10, 2014, http://www.nytimes.com/2014/03/11/business/energy-environment/coal- to-the-rescue-this-time.html?_r=0.

[71] Database of State Incentives for Renewables and Efficiency, Renewable Portfolio Standard Policies, March 2013, http://www.dsireusa.org/documents/summarymaps/RPS_map.pdf.

[72] American Council for an Energy-Efficient Economy, State Energy Efficiency Resource Standards, April 2014, http://www.aceee.org/files/pdf/policy-brief/eers-04-2014.pdf.

[73] Dwayne Stradford, The Revitalization, Modernization of the Aging Transmission System, Electric Light & Power, January 1, 2012, http://www.elp.com/articles/2012/01/the- revitalization-modernization-of-the-aging-transmissionsystem.html.

[74] See discussion of Order No. 1000 in CRS Report R41193, Electricity Transmission Cost Allocation, by Richard J. Campbell and Adam Vann.

[75] Generally, an Integrated Resource Plan is a 10- to 20-year look forward at options for meeting future energy demand which is revisited typically every three to five years to help ensure the continued validity of the planning process.

[76] EMEGU, p. 34855.

In: EPA's Proposed Carbon Dioxide Rule ...   ISBN: 978-1-63463-178-5
Editor: Carmella Ramos   © 2014 Nova Science Publishers, Inc.

Chapter 2

STATE CO_2 EMISSION RATE GOALS IN EPA'S PROPOSED RULE FOR EXISTING POWER PLANTS[*]

Jonathan L. Ramseur

SUMMARY

On June 18, 2014, the Environmental Protection Agency (EPA) published a proposed rulemaking that would establish guidelines for states to use when developing plans that address carbon dioxide (CO_2) emissions from existing fossil fuel-fired electric generating units. The proposal creates CO_2 emission rate goals—measured in pounds of CO_2 emissions per megawatts-hours (MWh) of electricity generation—for each state to achieve by 2030 and an interim goal to be achieved "on average" between 2020 and 2029. EPA estimates that if the states achieve their individual emission rate goals in 2030, the CO_2 emissions from the electric power sector in the United States would be reduced by 30% compared to 2005 levels.

This report discusses the methodology EPA used to establish state-specific CO_2 emission rate goals that apply to states' overall electricity generation portfolio.

The emission rate goals do not apply directly to individual emission sources. EPA established the emission rate goals by first determining

---

[*] This is an edited, reformatted and augmented version of a Congressional Research Service publication, No. R43652, dated July 21, 2014.

each state's 2012 emission rate baseline, which is generally a function of each state's portfolio of electricity generation in 2012. The resulting baselines in each state vary considerably, reflecting, among other things, the different energy sources used to generate electricity in each state.

To establish the emission rate goals, EPA applied four "building blocks" to the state baselines. The four building blocks involve estimates of various opportunities for states to decrease their emission rates:

- Building block 1: coal-fired power plant efficiency improvements;
- Building block 2: natural gas combined cycle displacement (NGCC) of more carbon-intensive sources, particularly coal;
- Building block 3: increased use of renewable energy and preservation of existing and under construction nuclear power; and
- Building block 4: energy efficiency improvements.

Building blocks 1 and 2 directly affect the CO_2 emission rate at affected EGUs by factoring in EGU efficiency improvements and opportunities to switch from high- to low-carbon power generation. In contrast, building blocks 3 and 4 involve so-called "outside the fence" opportunities that do not directly apply to electricity generation at affected EGUs.

The building blocks affect each state's emission rate in different ways, depending on each state's specific circumstances. On average, block 1 has the smallest average impact, decreasing state emission rate goals (compared to 2012 baselines) by a range of 0% to 6%.

Building block 2, on average, lowers rates by 13%, with a range of impacts from 0% to 38% (compared to baseline). The largest rate changes are seen in states that have both coal-fired EGUs and under-utilized NGCC plants. The smallest rate impacts are in states without any NGCC units and states that already have relatively high NGCC utilization rates.

The under construction nuclear component of building block 3 only affects rates in three states, but its rate impacts are considerable. An amount of at-risk nuclear generation was included in the 2012 baseline rates, lowering some state baselines by as much as 7%.

The renewable energy component of block 3, on average, reduces emission rate baselines by 9%, with a range from 2% to 33%. This block has a greater impact in states that use renewable energy (not counting hydroelectric power) to generate a substantial percentage of their total electricity.

Building block 4 reduces rates, on average, by 13%, with a range of impacts between 4% and 37%. This range is a result of several factors, including (1) the contribution of in-state electricity generation that comes from hydroelectric power or nuclear power; and (2) whether the state is a net importer or net exporter of electricity.

The results of applying the four building blocks do not require or predict a particular outcome in a state's electricity generation profile. The emission rates are a function of EPA's specific emission rate methodology. States may choose to meet emission rate goals by focusing on one or more of the building block strategies or through alternative approaches.

INTRODUCTION

On June 18, 2014, the Environmental Protection Agency (EPA) published in the *Federal Register* a proposed rulemaking[1] under Section 111(d) of the Clean Air Act.[2] The proposal would establish carbon dioxide (CO$_2$) emission guidelines for states to use when developing plans that address CO$_2$ emissions from existing fossil fuel-fired electric generating units.

The proposed rule establishes state-specific CO$_2$ emission rate goals, measured in pounds of CO$_2$ emissions per megawatt-hours (MWh) of electricity generation. This metric is generally described as carbon intensity, which is a ratio of CO$_2$ emissions per a unit of output, which is electric power (MWh) in this context. EPA based its intensity goals on each state's current portfolio of electricity generation and various assumptions involving opportunities for states to decrease their carbon intensity, including:

- coal-fired power plant efficiency improvements;
- natural gas combined cycle displacement of more carbon-intensive sources, particularly coal;
- increased use of low-carbon sources, namely renewable energies like wind and solar, and continued use of existing nuclear power generation; and
- energy efficiency improvements.

The proposal sets a final goal for each state[3] for 2030 and an interim goal to be achieved "on average" between 2020 and 2029.[4] EPA estimates that if the states achieve their individual emission rate goals in 2030, the CO$_2$ emissions from the electric power sector in the United States would be reduced by 30% compared to 2005 levels. However, the state emission rate goals are based on a baseline year of 2012, not 2005.

This report discusses the methodology EPA used to establish the state-specific CO_2 emission rate goals. The first section explains the process by which EPA created state-specific 2012 emission rate baselines. The emission rate equation EPA used to calculate the state baselines is provided at the end of this section.

The second section discusses the four categories of emission reduction opportunities, described as "building blocks" by EPA, that the agency used to determine the interim and 2030 emission rate goals for each state. The emission rate equation that incorporates each building block is provided at the end of this section.

In addition, **Table 6** at the end of this section lists the state-specific 2012 emission rate baselines, the final emission rate goals, and the incremental effects of applying each of EPA's building blocks to the 2012 baselines.

2012 EMISSION RATE BASELINE

EPA's first step in establishing the state-specific CO_2 emission rate goals involved setting state-specific baselines. The baseline is the starting point, from which future goals are measured. The baseline year selection is an important issue for some states, because some states already have regulations or policies that would directly (e.g., emissions cap) or indirectly (e.g., renewable portfolio standards) reduce CO_2 emissions. Some of these state requirements were in place well before 2012.

EPA chose to use state-specific data from 2012 to establish the rate-based baselines, stating:

> EPA chose the historic data approach as it reflected actual historic performance at the state level. EPA chose the year 2012 as it represented the most recent year for which complete data were available at the time of the analysis .... EPA also considered the possibility of using average fossil generation and emission rate values over a baseline period (e.g., 2009 – 2012), but determined that there would be little variation in results compared to a 2012 base year data set due to the rate-based nature of the goal.[5]

EPA Data Sources[6]

EPA used its Emissions & Generation Integrated Resource Database (eGRID) to provide the underlying data for the vast majority of the inputs the agency used to generate state emission rates. According to EPA, "eGRID integrates many different data sources on power plants and power companies, including, but not limited to: the EPA, the Energy Information Administration (EIA), the North American Electric Reliability Corporation (NERC), and the Federal Energy Regulatory Commission (FERC)."[7] In addition, EPA used its National Electric Energy Data System (NEEDS) to identify nuclear and NGCC plants that were not operating in 2012 but are under construction.

Affected EGUs

The 2012 state baselines are based on CO_2 emissions from electric generating units (EGUs) that are addressed in the proposal. These units are called "affected EGUs." The terminology in this proposal differs from other air pollutant regulations that apply directly to "covered sources" or "regulated entities." The emission rate goals described below do not apply directly to individual power plants, but to the state's overall electricity generation portfolio.

In general, an affected EGU is a fossil fuel-fired unit that was in operation or had commenced construction as of January 8, 2014, has a generating capacity above a certain threshold, and sells a certain amount of its electricity generation to the grid. The specific criteria include the following:

1) has a base load rating greater than 73 MW;
2) combusts fossil fuel for more than 10% of its total annual heat input; and
3) sells the greater of 219,000 MWh per year[8] or one-third of its potential electrical output to a utility distribution system.[9]

Based on 2012 data provided by EPA, the "affected EGU" definition applies to over 3,100 EGUs at 1,508 facilities throughout the United States.[10] The number of "affected" power plant facilities range by state, from 2 EGUs in Idaho to 115 EGUs in Texas, with a median number of 19.

Net Energy Output Versus Gross Output

In its proposed rule, EPA measures energy generation from affected EGUs in terms of net output rather than gross output. Gross output is the total amount of electricity (and/or useful thermal output)[11] that is produced at the generator terminal. Some of this gross output is used on-site to operate equipment at the EGU (e.g., pumps, fans, or pollution control devices).

Net output equals gross output minus the amount of energy used on-site, thus capturing only the electricity that is delivered to the transmission grid.

EPA explains that a net output measure would account for reduction opportunities in on-site energy use, which would not be captured using a gross output measure.[12] This would provide an incentive for on-site energy efficiency improvements. However, EPA notes that its proposed rule for new EGUs measures gross generation. The agency is requesting comment on the use of net generation for existing EGUs.

2012 Emission Rate Equation

EPA constructed the 2012 state baselines using CO_2 emissions and electricity generation data from the affected EGUs and several additional electricity generation categories described below.

First, EPA grouped the affected EGUs into different categories: coal-fired steam generation; oil and gas (OG) steam generation; natural gas combined cycle (NGCC) generation; and "other" affected EGUs. This last grouping includes fossil sources, such as integrated gasification combined cycle (IGCC) units, high utilization combustion turbine units, and applicable thermal output at cogeneration units.

EPA separated the data from these units because they are not part of the building block applications described below.[13] On a national basis, the "other" category accounts for approximately 1% of total U.S. electricity generation and CO_2 emissions.[14] And for the vast majority of states, these sources have minimal impacts on emission rates.

To establish each state's 2012 baseline, EPA calculated the pounds of CO_2 generated from affected EGUs in each state (the numerator in the **Table 1** equation)[15] and then divided that sum by the electricity generated (the denominator in the **Table 1** equation) from affected EGUs in each state.

Table 1. EPA's "Adjusted" 2012 Baseline Emission Rate Equation

$$\text{2012 Emission Rate} = \frac{\begin{array}{c}(\text{coal generation} \times \text{coal emission rate}) + (\text{OG generation} \times \text{OG emission rate}) + (\text{NGCC generation} \times \text{NGCC emission rate}) + \text{"Other" } CO_2 \text{ emissions}\end{array}}{\begin{array}{c}\text{coal generation} + \text{OG generation} + \text{NGCC generation} + \text{"Other" generation} + \text{"At-Risk" Nuclear} + \text{Renewable energy generation}\end{array}}$$

Notes: OG = oil and gas; NGCC = natural gas combined cycle; "other" generation includes fossil fuel EGUs, such as integrated gasification combined cycle (IGCC) units, high utilization combustion turbine units, and applicable thermal output at cogeneration units; "at-risk" nuclear includes 5.8% of a state's nuclear power capacity; renewable energy includes solar, wind, geothermal, wood and wood-derived fuels, other biomass, but not hydroelectric power.

This yields an emission rate measured in pounds (lbs.) of CO_2 per megawatt-hours (MWh) of electricity generation. EPA described this result as the "unadjusted" emission rate.

To establish the final, "adjusted" 2012 baseline for each state, EPA added two elements to the denominator of the emission rate equation (in **Table 1**): "at-risk" nuclear power (discussed below) and renewable energy generation. The addition of these elements produced the "adjusted" emission rate equation, which is used to generate the 2012 baseline emission rate for each state. The adjusted emission rate equation is provided below.

For the "at-risk" nuclear power element, EPA assumes that under a business-as-usual scenario some amount of existing nuclear power will be unavailable for use in the near future. Using projections from EIA, EPA determined that 5.8% of total U.S. nuclear power capacity was at risk of being retired in the near future.[16]

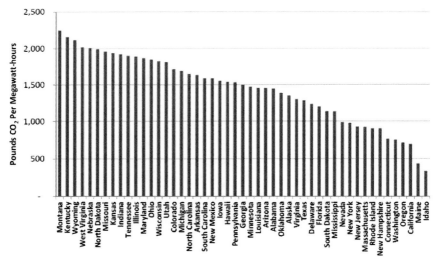

Source: Prepared by CRS.

Figure 1. EPA's 2012 State-Specific Emission Rate Baselines.

EPA used this percentage value to estimate at-risk nuclear power (in MWh) for each state with operating nuclear units in 2012.[17] According to EPA, this projected outcome is due to a "host of factors –increasing fixed operation and maintenance costs, relatively low wholesale electricity prices, and additional capital investment associated with ensuring plant security and emergency preparedness."

In addition, EPA added each state's renewable energy electricity generation (in MWh) from 2012 into the state baseline calculation.[18] As discussed below, renewable energy potential plays an important role in determining EPA's emission rate interim and final goals. Including renewable energy in the state baseline rates allows for a more appropriate comparison between the 2012 baseline and interim and final rate goals.

Applying the above equation to each state's specific circumstances yields a range of emission rate baselines, as illustrated in **Figure 1**.

CO_2 EMISSION RATE GOALS

In its proposed rule, EPA identified four categories of CO_2 emission reduction strategies that states could employ to reduce the states' overall CO_2 emission rates. EPA proposed that the combination of these four strategies—described as "building blocks"—represents the "best system of emission reduction...adequately demonstrated," a key determination pursuant to CAA Section 111(d).[19] Using the state-specific 2012 baseline data as its starting point, EPA applied the four building blocks to establish CO_2 emission rate goals for each state.

Building blocks 1 and 2 directly affect the CO_2 emission rate at affected EGUs by factoring in efficiency improvements at EGUs and opportunities to switch from high- to low-carbon power generation. In contrast, blocks 3 and 4 involve so-called "outside the fence" opportunities that do not directly apply to electricity generation at affected EGUs. These blocks decrease the states' overall CO_2 emission rates by (1) increasing the use of low- or zero-carbon electricity generation and (2) reducing consumer demand for electricity through energy efficiency improvements.

The equation for the 2030 emission rate goals, which includes the application of all four building blocks, is provided at the end of this section. Compared to the 2012 baseline emission rate equation, building blocks 3 and 4 add more elements to the equation's denominator. In its proposal, EPA explained:

> A goal expressed as an unadjusted output-weighted-average emission rate would fail to account for mass emission reductions from reductions in the total quantity of fossil fuel-fired generation associated with state plan

measures that increase low- or zero-carbon generating capacity [e.g., renewable portfolio standards] or demand-side energy efficiency. Accordingly, under the proposed goals, the emission rate computation includes an adjustment designed to reflect those mass emission reductions .... Mathematically, this adjustment has the effect of spreading the measured CO_2 emissions from the state's affected EGUs over a larger quantity of energy output, thus resulting in an adjusted mission rate lower than the unadjusted emission rate.

The following discussion describes each of these building blocks and their relative contributions to the state-specific emission rate goals.

Building Block 1—Coal-Fired Generation Efficiency Improvements

Building block 1 applies heat rate[20] (i.e., efficiency) improvements to coal-fired, steam EGUs. EPA maintains that these EGUs are "less efficient at converting fuel into electricity than is technically and economically possible."[21] Almost all of the existing coal-fired EGUs are considered steam EGUs. A small percentage of coal-fired EGUs are integrated gasification combined cycle (IGCC) units, but the proposed heat rate improvements in building block 1 do not apply to these units. EPA is seeking comment on whether the agency should include heat rate improvements at other fossil-fuel EGUs as part of its emission rate calculations.

Potential heat rate improvements include the adoption of operation and maintenance best practices and equipment upgrades. EPA determined that a combination of these potential options could improve coal-fired EGU heat rates by 6%. A reduction in the heat rate leads to a proportional reduction in CO_2 emissions, because CO_2 emissions are directly related to the amount of fuel consumed. Therefore, building block 1 reduces each state's CO_2 emissions rate (pounds of CO_2 per MWh) for coal-fired affected EGUs by as much as 6%.[22]

For example, if a state's coal-fired affected EGUs averaged 2,000 pounds of CO_2 emissions per MWh in 2012, building block 1 could decrease this rate to 1,880 pounds CO_2 per MWh. This lowers one of the elements ("coal emission rate") in the numerator of the emission rate equation (**Table 5**), but has no effect on the denominator.

As indicated in **Table 6**, building block 1 decreases state emission rate goals (compared to 2012 baselines) by a range of 0% to 6%. The greater rate impacts are seen in states that have a relatively high percentage of coal-fired electricity in their electricity generation portfolio.

Building Block 2—Increased Utilization of Natural Gas Combined Cycle Units

Building block 2 lowers a state's CO$_2$ emission rate (pounds of CO$_2$ per MWh) from the baseline by shifting a state's electricity generation from higher-carbon units, such as coal-fired EGUs, to lower-carbon NGCC units.[23] The carbon intensity of different types of EGUs can vary considerably. According to EPA,[24] the 2012 *average* CO$_2$ emission rates by unit type category were the following:

- Coal steam units = 2,220 lbs. CO$_2$/MWh
- Oil and natural gas steam units = 1,463 lbs. CO$_2$/MWh
- NGCC units = 907 lbs. CO$_2$/MWh

As electricity demand increases during the day, system operators or regional transmission organizations call into service ("dispatch") additional power plants to meet the electricity needs. When electricity demand decreases, these additional units are taken off-line. In general, coal-fired EGUs are dispatched before NGCC units, because coal-fired plants take hours or days to ramp up to their design capacity and they have traditionally been cheaper to operate than most other sources.

EPA concluded that there is "significant potential for re-dispatch" from steam EGUs to NGCC units.[25] The agency estimated that, in aggregate, NGCC units provided about 46% of their total generating capacity in 2012. This measure is called the capacity factor. Based on its analysis, EPA determined that a state's capacity factor for its NGCC units could be increased to 70%. Building block 2 uses the 70% capacity factor to increase the utilization of NGCC units and correspondingly decrease generation from more carbon intensive EGUs.

As an example, **Table 2** illustrates the application of building block 2 for Arizona. In 2012, NGCC units in Arizona generated 26.8 million MWh of electricity, which represented approximately 27% of the total NGCC nameplate capacity (11,202 MW) in the state.[26] Under building block 2 methodology, the increase in NGCC generation is capped at the lower of two ceilings: 70% of the nameplate capacity or the total generation from coal and

OG steam EGUs and NGCC units in 2012. Applying the 70% NGCC capacity factor would increase NGCC generation from 26.8 million MWh to 68.9 million MWh,[27] well above the total generation from all units in 2012 of 52.1 million MWh. Therefore, NGCC generation increases to 52.1 million MWh, the total generation from fossil fuel units in 2012. Applying block 2 methodology, the increased NGCC generation replaces generation from coal and OG steam EGUs, decreasing their generation to zero.

As **Table 2** indicates, building block 2 has a substantial effect on Arizona's emission rate, reducing it by 42%. Note that the results of applying building block 2 do not require or predict a particular outcome in a state's electricity generation profile. The results are a function of the emission rate methodology. States may choose to meet their emission rate goals through alternative approaches.

Table 6 shows the effect that building blocks 1-2 have on all of the 2012 state emission rate baselines.

Table 2. Illustration of Building Block 2 for Arizona's Emission Rate Goal

	2012 Baseline	After Building Block 2
Coal steam generation	24.3 million MWh	0
OG steam generation	1.0 million MWh	0
NGCC generation	26.8 million MWh	52.1 million MWh
Total generation	52.1 million MWh	52.1 million MWh
NGCC capacity factor	27%	53%
Emissions Rate	1,453 lbs. CO_2/MWh	843 lbs. CO_2/MWh
NGCC nameplate capacity = 11,202 MW		

Source: Prepared by CRS; data from EPA Proposed Rule, technical support documents and spreadsheets, at http://www2.epa.gov/carbon

Building Block 3—Renewable Energy and Nuclear Power

Building block 3 factors in additional electricity generation from low- or zero-carbon emitting sources, including renewable energy and nuclear power. Both types of generation are added to the denominator for the emission rate equation (see **Table 5** at the end of this section), but the numerator is unchanged. The methodologies for incorporating these categories of electricity generation are very different, thus they are discussed separately below.

Renewable Energy

Building block 3 projects annual renewable energy (RE) increases for each state. Current RE use varies by states and the potential to utilize different types of renewable energy sources—wind, solar, geothermal—varies by geographic location. To "account for similar power system characteristics as well as geographic similarities in [renewable energy] potential,"[28] As illustrated in **Figure 2**, EPA placed each state into one of six regions (Alaska and Hawaii have individual targets). EPA determined a RE 2030 target for each region based on an average of existing RE targets that are required by states in the relevant region.[29] Then, EPA calculated an annual growth rate for each region that would allow each region to reach its specific target by 2030.

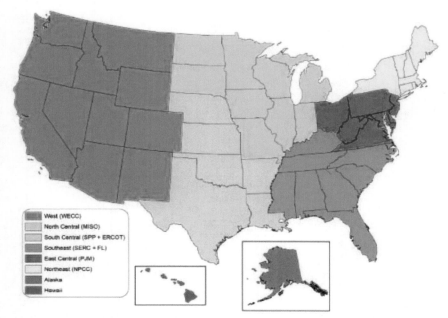

Source: Figure 4-3 from EPA, Technical Support Document, *GHG Abatement Measures*.

Figure 2. EPA's Proposed Regions in its Renewable Energy Methodology.

Table 3 lists the six regions and their states, the regional targets, and the average annual growth rates for each region. The regional targets range from 10% to 25%, and the growth rates range from 6% to 17%. As the table indicates, a region can have a relatively high regional target (e.g., the West region's target of 21%) but have a relatively low growth rate (6% in the West region).

Table 3. Renewable Energy Regions, Targets, and Growth Rates

Region	States	Regional Target	Average Annual Growth Rate
East Central	Delaware, District of Columbia, Maryland, New Jersey, Ohio, Pennsylvania, Virginia, and West Virginia	16%	17%
North Central	Illinois, Indiana, Iowa, Michigan, Minnesota, Missouri, North Dakota, South Dakota, and Wisconsin	15%	6%
Northeast	Connecticut, Maine, Massachusetts, New Hampshire, New York, Rhode Island, and Vermont	25%	13%
South Central	Arkansas, Kansas, Louisiana, Nebraska, Oklahoma, and Texas	20%	8%
Southeast	Alabama, Florida, Georgia, Kentucky, Mississippi, North Carolina, South Carolina, and Tennessee	10%	13%
West	Arizona, California, Colorado, Idaho, Montana, Nevada, New Mexico, Oregon, Utah, Washington, and Wyoming	21%	6%
	Alaska	10%	11%
	Hawaii	10%	8%

Source: Prepared by EPA; data from EPA, Technical Support Document, Greenhouse Gas Abatement Measures.

Notes: Although Vermont does not have an emission rate goal, EPA included Vermont's RE generation when the agency determined the annual growth rate for the Northeast region. If Vermont's RE generation is excluded, the annual growth rate increases slightly, but remains at 13%.

Conversely, a state can have a relatively low target (10% in the Southeast region) and a relatively high growth rate (13% in the Southeast region). These outcomes are a function of EPA's methodology. For instance, the West region's growth rate is relatively low, because some of the states—namely California, which accounts for 28% of the region's total electricity generation— are more than halfway toward the regional goal. In contrast, the states in the Southeast are starting with relatively low percentages (0% to 3%) of RE generation in 2012, which accounts for the relatively high growth rate needed to achieve their regional target.

EPA applies the region-specific, annual growth rate to each state's RE generation in 2012 to estimate annual RE generation for each state from 2017 through 2030.[30] If a state's RE use equals or exceeds its 2030 regional target, the state's RE use is held constant at the level that matches its regional target.

The 2012 RE baseline does not include hydroelectric generation.[31] According to EPA:

> Inclusion of this generation in current and projected levels of performance would distort the proposed approach by presuming future development potential of large hydroelectric capacity in other states. Because RPS [renewable portfolio standard] policies were implemented to stimulate the development of new RE generation, existing hydroelectric facilities are often excluded from RPS accounting. No states are expected to develop any new large facilities.[32]

Although EPA's determination of regional RE targets does not explicitly account for opportunities to build new hydroelectric facilities,[33] states could use increased hydroelectric power generation in the future to lower their emission rate.

Table 4 applies EPA's methodology and depicts the states' RE levels in 2012, total electricity generation in 2012, and the percentage of electricity generation from renewable sources in 2012 and 2030. The last column measures the projected RE generation in 2030 against the total electricity generation in 2012.

EPA's RE building block 3 methodology yields the following results:

- About half of the states would not reach their region-specific goals by 2030; the other half would reach the region-specific goals. Some of these states reached their goals in the early years. In general, the percentage of electricity generated from renewable sources in these states was relatively high in the baseline year (2012);

- Five states—Iowa, Maine, Minnesota, North Dakota, and South Dakota— matched or exceeded their regional RE targets in 2012, so the estimated future RE generation (for the purposes of the emission rate calculations) in these states actually *decreases* to match their regional targets. Arguably, this outcome artificially lowers the emission rate targets for these states and EPA specifically asks for comment on whether the calculations should include a RE floor based on 2012 generation; and
- The impact of building block 3 varies considerably by states. Not counting the states that meet or exceed their targets in 2012, some states increase their percentages of RE generation by 2%; others increase their percentages by over 18%. These different impacts are reflected in **Table 6**, which shows the emission rate change after applying blocks 1-3.

Table 4. Renewable Energy Generation
States Grouped in Their Renewable Energy Regions

State	2012 RE Generation (MWh)	2012 Total Electricity Generation (MWh)	Percent of RE Generation in 2012	Percent of RE Generation in 2030
Region: East Central – Target 16% – Annual Growth Rate 17%				
Delaware	131,051	8,633,694	2%	12%
Maryland	898,152	37,809,744	2%	16%
New Jersey	1,280,715	65,263,408	2%	16%
Ohio	1,738,622	29,745,731	1%	11%
Pennsylvania	4,459,118	23,419,715	2%	16%
Virginia	2,358,444	70,739,235	3%	16%
West Virginia	1,296,563	73,413,405	2%	14%
Region: North Central –Target 15% – Annual Growth Rate 6%				
Illinois	8,372,660	197,565,363	4%	9%
Indiana	3,546,367	114,695,729	3%	7%
Iowa	14,183,424	56,675,404	25%	15%
Michigan	3,785,439	108,166,078	3%	7%
Minnesota	9,453,871	52,193,624	18%	15%
Missouri	1,298,579	91,804,321	1%	3%
North Dakota	5,280,052	36,125,159	15%	15%

State	2012 RE Generation (MWh)	2012 Total Electricity Generation (MWh)	Percent of RE Generation in 2012	Percent of RE Generation in 2030
South Dakota	2,914,666	12,034,206	24%	15%
Wisconsin	3,223,178	63,742,910	5%	11%
Region: Northeast – Target 25% – Annual Growth Rate 13%				
Connecticut	666,525	36,117,544	2%	9%
Maine	4,098,795	14,428,596	28%	25%
Massachusetts	1,843,419	36,198,121	5%	24%
New Hampshire	1,381,285	19,264,435	7%	25%
New York	5,192,427	135,768,251	4%	18%
Rhode Island	101,895	8,309,036	1%	6%
Vermont	465,169	6,569,670	7%	25%
Region: South Central – Target 20% – Annual Growth Rate 8%				
Arkansas	1,660,370	65,005,678	3%	7%
Kansas	5,252,653	44,424,691	12%	20%
Louisiana	2,430,042	103,407,706	2%	7%
Nebraska	1,346,762	34,217,293	4%	11%
Oklahoma	8,520,724	77,896,588	11%	20%
Texas	34,016,697	429,812,510	8%	20%
Region: Southeast – Target 10% – Annual Growth Rate 13%				
Alabama	2,776,554	152,878,688	2%	9%
Florida	4,523,798	221,096,136	2%	10%
Georgia	3,278,536	122,306,364	3%	10%
Kentucky	332,879	89,949,689	0.4%	2%
Mississippi	1,509,190	54,584,295	3%	10%
North Carolina	2,703,919	116,681,763	2%	10%
South Carolina	2,143,473	96,755,682	2%	10%
Tennessee	836,458	77,724,264	1%	6%
Region: West – Target 21% – Annual Growth Rate 6%				
Arizona	1,697,652	95,016,925	2%	4%
California	29,966,846	199,518,567	15%	21%
Colorado	6,192,082	52,556,701	12%	21%
Idaho	2,514,502	15,499,089	16%	21%
Montana	1,261,752	27,804,784	5%	10%
Nevada	2,968,630	35,173,263	8%	18%

Table 4. (Continued)

State	2012 RE Generation (MWh)	2012 Total Electricity Generation (MWh)	Percent of RE Generation in 2012	Percent of RE Generation in 2030
New Mexico	2,573,851	22,894,524	11%	21%
Oregon	7,207,229	60,932,715	12%	21%
Utah	1,099,724	36,312,527	3%	7%
Washington	8,214,350	116,835,474	7%	15%
Wyoming	4,369,107	49,588,606	9%	19%
Alaska	39,958	6,946,419	1%	2%
Hawaii	924,815	10,469,269	9%	10%

Source: Prepared by CRS; data from EPA, Technical Support Document, Greenhouse Gas Abatement Measures, which uses data from EIA, "Net Generation by State by Type of Producer by Energy," at http://www.eia.gov/electricity

Notes: RE generation includes solar, wind, geothermal, wood and wood-derived fuels, other biomass, but not hydroelectric power. The "total electricity generation" data include generation from multiple sources, including both affected and non-affected fossil-fired EGUs, the above renewable energy sources and hydroelectric power. The column labeled "Percent of RE Generation in 2030" measures the projected RE generation (MWh) in 2030 compared to the total MWh of electricity generated in 2012.

Although Vermont does not have an emission rate goal, EPA included Vermont's RE generation when the agency determined the annual growth rate for the Northeast region. If Vermont's RE generation is excluded, the annual growth rate increases slightly, but remains at 13%.

Nuclear Energy

The second part of building block 3 involves nuclear power generation. EPA includes both "at-risk" and "under construction" nuclear power in the denominator of the emission rate equation (see **Table 5** at the end of this section). As discussed above, the "at-risk" nuclear power, which exists in 30 states, was factored into the state 2012 baseline emission rates. Thus, its inclusion in the emission rate goal equation has no effect on the emission rate compared to the 2012 baseline.[34] However, its inclusion in the 2012 baseline equation was unique: it was the only part of the baseline equation that projected future activity (i.e., loss of nuclear power capacity). Thus, if states do not maintain their existing nuclear generation, their emission rates will increase (all else being equal). Including at-risk nuclear generation in the baseline equation denominator was one of EPA's "adjustments." The at-risk nuclear generations lowered the (unadjusted) baselines in some states by as much as 7%, thus having a stronger impact that building block 1.

In addition to the "at-risk" nuclear power, EPA added projected electricity generation from nuclear power units that are currently under construction. EPA identified five under-construction nuclear units at three facilities in Georgia, South Carolina, and Tennessee. The estimated electric generation from these units and their percentage contribution to the state's total electricity generation in 2012 are listed below:

- Georgia: approximately 17 million MWh (14% of total electric generation in 2012)
- South Carolina: approximately 17 million MWh (18% of total electric generation in 2012);
- Tennessee: approximately 9 million MWh (11% of total electric generation in 2012).

Including the estimated generation from these anticipated units in the emission rate equation substantially lowers the emission rates of these three states (**Table 6**). If these anticipated units do not complete construction and enter service, these states would likely have more difficulty achieving their emission rate goals.

Building Block 4—Energy Efficiency Improvements

The fourth building block reduces state emission rates by including avoided electricity generation that results from projected energy efficiency (EE) improvements. These EE improvements are described as "demand-side," because they would seek to reduce the demand for electricity from end-users, such as factories, office buildings, and homes. EPA estimated the amount of decreased electricity generation in each state that would result from EE activities and added the avoided MWh to the denominator of the emission rate equation (**Table 5**).

Demand-side EE activities can involve a range of practices in the residential, commercial, and industrial sectors. According to EPA, "every state has established demand-side energy efficiency policies."[35] However, these policies cover a wide range of activities, and, as discussed below, their effectiveness varies. EPA states that the "most prominent and impactful" EE policies in most states are those that the drive development and funding of EE programs and building codes.[36]

To estimate the avoided electricity generation, EPA first determined the "best practices" performance target for all states. Using data from EIA,[37] EPA calculated each state's incremental EE savings as a percentage of retail electricity sales. According to EPA, "incremental savings (also known as first-year savings) represent the reduction in electricity use in a given year associated with new EE activities in that same year." As **Figure 3** illustrates, the states' 2012 incremental EE savings ranged from 0% to 2.19%.

In addition to the three states—Vermont, Maine, and Arizona—that achieved EE savings greater than 1.5% (**Figure 3**), EPA concluded that nine other states are expected to reach this annual level of performance by 2020.[38] Based on these observed and expected achievements, EPA determined that the "best practices" performance target for all states should be 1.5%. **Figure 3** depicts this performance target as a red line. EPA explained:

> [The best practices scenario] does not represent an EPA forecast of business-as-usual impacts of state energy efficiency policies or an EPA estimate of the full potential of end-use energy efficiency available to the power system, but rather represents a feasible policy scenario showing the reductions in fossil fuel-fired electricity generation resulting from accelerated use of energy efficiency policies in all states consistent with a level of performance that has already been achieved or required by policies (e.g., energy efficiency resource standards) of the leading states.[39]

Similar to the RE methodology described above, EPA's calculations assume that the EE component of the rate equation begins in 2017, and states would start that year at the EE incremental saving levels achieved in 2012 (**Figure 3**). EPA points out that EE improvements made between 2012 and 2017 would count toward achieving a state's emission rate target. However, if a state were to decrease its actual EE performance prior to 2017, the state would face a more difficult effort (all else being equal) in achieving its emission rate goal, as its 2017 EE starting point would be based on its (higher) 2012 EE performance level.

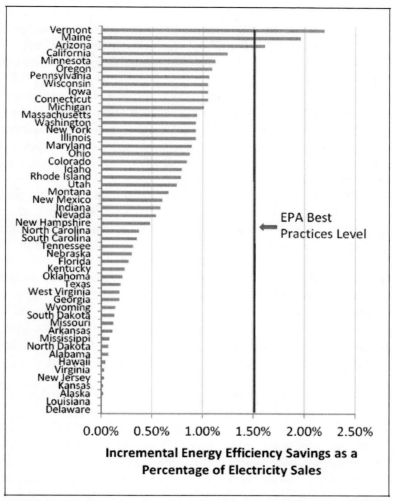

Source: Prepared by CRS; data from EPA, Technical Support Document, Greenhouse Gas Abatement Measures. EPA used data from EIA Form 861, which includes retail electricity sales and incremental electricity savings from energy efficiency, available at http://www.eia.gov/electricity/data/eia861/index.html.

Notes: Although Vermont does not have an emission rate goal, EPA included its EE performance in its best practice analysis.

Figure 3. Incremental Energy Efficiency Savings in 2012 by State; Compared to EPA's Best Practices Level.

The next determination made by EPA was the pace at which states, starting in 2017, would annually increase their EE incremental performance. Based on its analysis of historical EE performance increases and future requirements for some states, EPA chose an annual increase of 0.2%, which it deemed as a "conservative" value.

EPA assumed that each state would increase its incremental EE performance by 0.2% each year, starting in 2018, until it reached the best practices, incremental target of 1.5%. EPA projects that a small number of states would achieve this level in 2017, with the rest of the states reaching this level by 2025. Once this level is achieved, EPA assumed the states could sustain that incremental performance level through 2030.

Next, EPA estimated the cumulative savings that each state would achieve through its annual, incremental EE efforts. In contrast to incremental savings, which measure EE improvements made in one specific year, cumulative savings include the aggregate impacts of EE improvements made in prior years.

This raises the question: how many years are counted in the cumulative savings tally? For instance, the installation of a high-efficiency appliance may yield EE savings for the life of the appliance (e.g., 10-15 years), referred to as its "measure life." Other improvements (e.g., home insulation, building codes) may provide savings for twenty years or more. Based on its analysis of various studies, EPA determined the average measure life for an EE portfolio would be 10 years.

However, in its EE methodology, EPA distributed the decline in EE savings over 20 years, instead of having 10 years of savings and then dropping to zero at year 11. Both approaches lead to the same overall EE savings, but EPA's approach spreads the savings over a longer period of time.

EPA used the above inputs to estimate cumulative EE savings, as a percentage of retail sales, for each state for each year between 2020 and 2030. This calculation combined the above state-specific inputs with business-as-usual regional estimates of electricity retail sales.[40] Based on EPA's estimates, the EE improvements would yield cumulative reductions in electricity generation in the range of 9% to 12% by 2030, depending on the state's EE starting point.

EPA applied each state's annual (2020-2029) cumulative reductions (as a percentage of sales) to the amount of total electricity (including hydropower) sold to in-state consumers in 2012. EPA adjusted this value to account for states that are net importers or exporters of electricity.

Some states (e.g., Idaho and Delaware) import close to 50% of the electricity sold in their state. Other states (e.g., North Dakota, Wyoming, and West Virginia) generate more than twice the amount of electricity they use in-state, exporting the additional electricity to neighboring states.

For net importers, EPA adjusted the cumulative reductions by applying the cumulative reduction percentage to in-state sales, multiplied by the in-state generation as a percentage of sales. For example, Delaware's in-state generation as a percentage of sales equaled 45%, meaning it imported 55% of its total electricity in 2012. To calculate Delaware's cumulative EE reductions, EPA multiplied Delaware's electricity sales (12 million MWh) by its generation as a percentage of sales (0.45) by its cumulative EE reduction percentage (9.5% in 2029).

For net exporters, the EE cumulative reduction percentages only apply to in-state electricity sales, not the total amount of electricity generated. The resulting avoided electricity generation values for each state are added to the denominator in the emission rate equation (**Table 5**).

The impacts of applying building block 4 to the emission rate equation vary by state. In general, the effects appear to be more pronounced in states that generate a large percentage of their electricity from sources that are not already included in the emission rate equation. This primarily involves hydroelectric power, and to some extent, nuclear power generation. For example, building block 4 appears to have a greater effect in Washington (77% of total power generation from hydropower), Idaho (71% from hydropower), and Oregon (65% from hydropower).

Building block 4 includes hydroelectric power generation as part of the total generation subject to EE reductions, but this is the only instance in which MWh from hydroelectric power generation are part of the emission rate equation.

In addition, the EE methodology appears to have a greater effect in states with relatively high percentages of nuclear power generation, such as South Carolina (53% nuclear power) and New Jersey (51% nuclear power). Although existing nuclear power is captured in the emission rate equation, it only accounts for the at-risk (5.8%) component.

By comparison, the effects of building block 4 are less pronounced in states that export a substantial amount of the electricity they generate, such as Wyoming, North Dakota, and West Virginia. These states generate more than twice as much electricity as they consume.

The total generation from affected EGUs is captured in the equation's numerator, but only the avoided generation from in-state sales is captured in the denominator, resulting in a lesser impact from building block 4.

What do the different effects of the EE building block mean for states? The states that generate a considerable percentage of electricity from either hydroelectric power or nuclear power may have more limited options to find emission rate reductions than other states.

The inclusion of avoided generation from all electricity generating sources may compel these states to focus on EE improvements to reach their emission rate targets.

This potential outcome assumes these states cannot find rate reductions from their existing hydroelectric or nuclear power sources.

CONCLUSION

As **Table 6** indicates, the building blocks affect each state's emission rate baseline in different ways, depending on each state's specific electricity generation circumstances. **Table 6** presents an incremental analysis of the impacts of applying the building blocks in a stepwise fashion (or all at once), ultimately reaching the 2030 emission rate goal.

As another measure of a state-by-state comparison, CRS used EPA's emission rate methodology to calculate the impacts of each building block *in isolation*.

The results are listed in **Table 7**. These calculations illustrate the relative impacts of the four building blocks for each state. For example in Idaho, building blocks 1, 2, and 3 (nuclear) have no impact on the 2012 emission rate, because Idaho has no coal-fired EGUs, no room to improve its NGCC utilization, and no nuclear generation. Therefore, the only impacts to its 2012 baseline rate are due to the renewable component of building block 3 and EE improvements from building block 4.

As **Table 7** indicates, on average, building block 1 has the smallest impact (4%), decreasing state emission rate goals (compared to 2012 baselines) by a range of 0% to 6%.

The emission rates in states (e.g., Rhode Island, Maine, and Idaho) without coal-fired, steam EGUs are unaffected by this block; states that employ coal-fired units to generate a significant percentage of their electricity (e.g., Kentucky, West Virginia, and Wyoming) see a greater impact to their emission rates.

Building block 2, on average, generates the largest (tied with block 4 below) incremental impact (13%), ranging from a 0% to 38% change (compared to baseline).

The largest changes are seen in states that have both coal-fired EGUs and under-utilized NGCC plants. The smallest impacts are in states without any NGCC and states that already have relatively high NGCC utilization rates.

Although the nuclear component of building block 3 only affects three states, its impacts are considerable in those states.

The RE component of building block 3, on average, reduces emission rate baselines by 9% (10% if the negative values are omitted). The impacts from the RE block application range from 2% to 33%. Multiple factors explain this range of impacts.

For example, this block has a considerable effect in Washington (33%), because it increases the state's RE generation by 116% and RE accounts for a substantial percentage of the state's total generation (not counting hydroelectric power): 30% in 2012 and 65% in 2030. Although Kentucky's RE generation increases by 415% between 2012 and 2030 (from 0.4% to 2%), the RE block has a relatively small impact, because RE continues to account for a small percentage of the state's total generation.

Building block 4 has the largest impact (tied with block 2) on emission rate baselines, reducing them, on average, by 13%, but the range of impacts is between 4% and 37%.

This range is a result of several factors, including (1) the contribution of in-state electricity generation that comes from hydroelectric power or nuclear power; and (2) whether the state is a net importer or net exporter of electricity.

Although the isolated building block application (in **Table 7**) provides a comparison of the relative magnitude of potential effects in each state, states have the flexibility to combine the building blocks (and/or other potential activities) to meet their emission rate targets. EPA's building blocks were meant to establish the emission rate goals, not predict a particular outcome in a state's electricity generation profile.

Table 5. Equation for CO2 Emission Rate Goals Building Block (BB) Adjustments

$$\text{2030 Emission Rate Goal} = \frac{\begin{array}{l}[\text{coal generation (\textbf{BB2})} \times \text{coal emission rate (\textbf{BB1})}] + [\text{OG generation (\textbf{BB2})} \times \text{OG emission rate}] \\ + [\text{NGCC generation (\textbf{BB2})} \times \text{NGCC emission rate}] + \text{``Other'' CO}_2\text{ emissions}\end{array}}{\begin{array}{l}\text{coal generation (\textbf{BB2})} + \text{OG generation (\textbf{BB2})} + \text{NGCC generation (\textbf{BB2})} + \text{``Other'' generation} \\ + \text{``At-risk'' and under construction nuclear generation (\textbf{BB3})} + \text{Renewable energy generation (\textbf{BB3})} \\ + \text{Avoided generation from energy efficiency (\textbf{BB4})}\end{array}}$$

Source: Prepared by CRS; additional information in EPA, *Goal Computation Technical Support Document*, at http://www2.epa.gov/carbon-

Notes: OG = oil and gas; NGCC = natural gas combined cycle; "other" generation includes fossil fuel EGUs, such as integrated gasification combined cycle (IGCC) units, high utilization combustion turbine units, and applicable thermal output at cogeneration units; "at-risk" nuclear includes 5.8% of a state's nuclear power capacity; renewable energy includes solar, wind, geothermal, wood and wood-derived fuels, other biomass, but not hydroelectric power.

Table 6. 2012 State Emission Rate Baselines and Building Block Applications
Emission rate baselines in pounds of CO_2 emissions per MWh

State	2012 Emission Rate Baseline	Block 1	Blocks 1-2	Blocks 1-3	Blocks 1-4 (2030 Emissions Rate Goal)	Percent Reduction from 2012 Baseline
Alabama	1,444	1,385	1,264	1,139	1,059	27%
Alaska	1,351	1,340	1,237	1,191	1,003	26%
Arizona	1,453	1,394	843	814	702	52%
Arkansas	1,634	1,554	1,058	996	910	44%
California	698	697	662	615	537	23%
Colorado	1,714	1,621	1,334	1,222	1,108	35%
Connecticut	765	764	733	643	540	29%
Delaware	1,234	1,211	996	892	841	32%
Florida	1,199	1,169	882	812	740	38%
Georgia	1,500	1,433	1,216	926	834	44%
Hawaii	1,540	1,512	1,512	1,485	1,306	15%
Idaho	339	339	339	291	228	33%
Illinois	1,894	1,784	1,614	1,476	1,271	33%
Indiana	1,924	1,817	1,772	1,707	1,531	20%
Iowa	1,552	1,461	1,304	1,472	1,301	16%
Kansas	1,940	1,828	1,828	1,658	1,499	23%
Kentucky	2,158	2,028	1,978	1,947	1,763	18%
Louisiana	1,455	1,404	1,043	978	883	39%
Maine	437	437	425	451	378	14%
Maryland	1,870	1,772	1,722	1,394	1,187	37%
Massachusetts	925	915	819	661	576	38%

Table 6. (Continued)

State	2012 Emission Rate Baseline	Block 1	Blocks 1-2	Blocks 1-3	Blocks 1-4 (2030 Emissions Rate Goal)	Percent Reduction from 2012 Baseline
Michigan	1,690	1,603	1,408	1,339	1,161	31%
Minnesota	1,470	1,389	999	1,042	873	41%
Mississippi	1,093	1,071	809	752	692	37%
Missouri	1,963	1,849	1,742	1,711	1,544	21%
Montana	2,246	2,114	2,114	1,936	1,771	21%
Nebraska	2,009	1,889	1,803	1,652	1,479	26%
Nevada	988	970	799	720	647	35%
New Hampshire	905	887	710	532	486	46%
New Jersey	928	916	811	616	531	43%
New Mexico	1,586	1,513	1,277	1,163	1,048	34%
New York	978	970	828	652	549	44%
North Carolina	1,647	1,560	1,248	1,125	992	40%
North Dakota	1,994	1,875	1,875	1,865	1,783	11%
Ohio	1,850	1,751	1,673	1,512	1,338	28%
Oklahoma	1,387	1,334	1,053	964	895	35%
Oregon	717	701	565	452	372	48%
Pennsylvania	1,531	1,458	1,393	1,157	1,052	31%
Rhode Island	907	907	907	867	782	14%
South Carolina	1,587	1,506	1,342	866	772	51%
South Dakota	1,135	1,067	732	900	741	35%
Tennessee	1,903	1,797	1,698	1,322	1,163	39%
Texas	1,284	1,235	979	861	791	38%

State	2012 Emission Rate Baseline	Block 1	Blocks 1-2	Blocks 1-3	Blocks 1-4 (2030 Emissions Rate Goal)	Percent Reduction from 2012 Baseline
Utah	1,813	1,713	1,508	1,454	1,322	27%
Virginia	1,302	1,258	1,047	894	810	38%
Washington	756	728	444	298	215	72%
West Virginia	2,019	1,898	1,898	1,687	1,620	20%
Wisconsin	1,827	1,728	1,487	1,379	1,203	34%
Wyoming	2,115	1,988	1,957	1,771	1,714	19%

Source: Prepared by CRS; data from EPA, Goal Computation Technical Support Document, at http://www2.epa.gov/carbon

Notes: EPA did not establish emission rate goals for Vermont and the District of Columbia because they do not currently have affected EGUs.

Table 7. Application of EPA's Building Blocks *in Isolation*

State	2012 Emission Rate Baseline	Block 1	Percent Reduction from Baseline	Block 2	Percent Reduction from Baseline	Block 3 (Nuclear)	Percent Reduction from Baseline	Block 3 (Renewables)	Percent Reduction from Baseline	Block 4	Percent Reduction from Baseline
Alabama	1,444	1,385	4%	1,311	9%	1,444	0%	1,301	10%	1,332	8%
Alaska	1,351	1,340	1%	1,237	8%	1,351	0%	1,301	4%	1,131	16%
Arizona	1,453	1,394	4%	843	42%	1,453	0%	1,404	3%	1,247	14%
Arkansas	1,634	1,554	5%	1,087	34%	1,634	0%	1,538	6%	1,485	9%
California	698	697	0%	662	5%	698	0%	645	7%	598	14%
Colorado	1,714	1,621	5%	1,394	19%	1,714	0%	1,567	9%	1,538	10%
Connecticut	765	764	0%	733	4%	765	0%	671	12%	629	18%

Table 7. (Continued)

State	2012 Emission Rate Baseline	Block 1	Percent Reduction from Baseline	Block 2	Percent Reduction from Baseline	Block 3 (Nuclear)	Percent Reduction from Baseline	Block 3 (Renewables)	Percent Reduction from Baseline	Block 4	Percent Reduction from Baseline
Delaware	1,234	1,211	2%	999	19%	1,234	0%	1,105	10%	1,156	6%
Florida	1,199	1,169	3%	885	26%	1,199	0%	1,101	8%	1,083	10%
Georgia	1,500	1,433	5%	1,261	16%	1,243	17%	1,355	10%	1,310	13%
Hawaii	1,540	1,512	2%	1,540	0%	1,540	0%	1,512	2%	1,350	12%
Idaho	339	339	0%	339	0%	339	0%	291	14%	257	24%
Illinois	1,894	1,784	6%	1,705	10%	1,894	0%	1,732	9%	1,609	15%
Indiana	1,924	1,817	6%	1,874	3%	1,924	0%	1,853	4%	1,719	11%
Iowa	1,552	1,461	6%	1,377	11%	1,552	0%	1,752	-13%	1,390	10%
Kansas	1,940	1,828	6%	1,940	0%	1,940	0%	1,759	9%	1,738	10%
Kentucky	2,158	2,028	6%	2,093	3%	2,158	0%	2,123	2%	1,944	10%
Louisiana	1,455	1,404	3%	1,067	27%	1,455	0%	1,364	6%	1,305	10%
Maine	437	437	0%	424	3%	437	0%	465	-6%	370	16%
Maryland	1,870	1,772	5%	1,815	3%	1,870	0%	1,513	19%	1,538	18%
Massachusetts	925	915	1%	819	11%	925	0%	747	19%	781	16%
Michigan	1,690	1,603	5%	1,476	13%	1,690	0%	1,607	5%	1,456	14%
Minnesota	1,470	1,389	5%	1,038	29%	1,470	0%	1,533	-4%	1,239	16%
Mississippi	1,093	1,071	2%	809	28%	1,130	0%	1,040	8%	1,020	10%
Missouri	1,963	1,849	6%	1,844	6%	1,963	0%	1,928	2%	1,769	10%
Montana	2,246	2,114	6%	2,246	0%	2,246	0%	2,058	8%	2,038	10%
Nebraska	2,009	1,889	6%	1,910	5%	2,009	0%	1,840	8%	2,038	11%
Nevada	988	970	2%	799	19%	988	0%	890	10%	878	11%

State	2012 Emission Rate Baseline	Block 1	Percent Reduction from Baseline	Block 2	Percent Reduction from Baseline	Block 3 (Nuclear)	Percent Reduction from Baseline	Block 3 (Renewables)	Percent Reduction from Baseline	Block 4	Percent Reduction from Baseline
New Hampshire	905	887	2%	710	22%	905	0%	678	25%	804	11%
New Jersey	928	916	1%	811	13%	928	0%	704	24%	766	17%
New Mexico	1,586	1,513	5%	1,326	16%	1,586	0%	1,444	9%	1,415	11%
New York	978	970	1%	828	15%	978	0%	771	21%	790	19%
North Carolina	1,647	1,560	5%	1,298	21%	1,647	0%	1,463	11%	1,407	15%
North Dakota	1,994	1,875	6%	1,994	0%	1,994	0%	1,984	1%	1,907	4%
Ohio	1,850	1,751	5%	1,763	5%	1,850	0%	1,669	10%	1,613	13%
Oklahoma	1,387	1,334	4%	1,079	22%	1,387	0%	1,269	8%	1,280	8%
Oregon	717	701	2%	565	21%	717	0%	573	20%	565	21%
Pennsylvania	1,531	1,458	5%	1,458	5%	1,531	0%	1,272	17%	1,367	11%
Rhode Island	907	907	0%	907	0%	907	0%	867	4%	814	10%
South Carolina	1,587	1,506	5%	1,406	11%	1,147	28%	1,361	14%	1,335	16%
South Dakota	1,135	1,067	6%	754	34%	1,135	0%	1,395	-23%	965	15%
Tennessee	1,903	1,797	6%	1,794	6%	1,581	17%	1,762	7%	1,618	15%
Texas	1,284	1,235	4%	1,002	22%	1,284	0%	1,129	12%	1,167	9%
Utah	1,813	1,713	6%	1,584	13%	1,813	0%	1,748	4%	1,643	9%
Virginia	1,302	1,258	3%	1,067	18%	1,302	0%	1,076	17%	1,133	13%
Washington	756	728	4%	444	41%	756	0%	506	33%	479	37%
West Virginia	2,019	1,898	6%	2,019	0%	2,019	0%	1,794	11%	1,929	4%

Table 7. (Continued)

State	2012 Emission Rate Baseline	Block 1	Percent Reduction from Baseline	Block 2	Percent Reduction from Baseline	Block 3 (Nuclear)	Percent Reduction from Baseline	Block 3 (Renewables)	Percent Reduction from Baseline	Block 4	Percent Reduction from Baseline
Wisconsin	1,827	1,728	5%	1,561	15%	1,827	0%	1,694	7%	1,577	14%
Wyoming	2,115	1,988	6%	2,075	2%	2,115	0%	1,911	10%	2,039	4%
Average			4%		13%		1%		9%		13%

Source: Prepared by CRS; data from EPA, technical support document spreadsheets, at http://www2.epa.gov/carbon-

Notes: Using EPA's emission rate formula and underlying data (provided in EPA spreadsheets), CRS calculated the impacts that each building block would have on the emission rate baselines. The building block applications examine their impacts in isolation. For example, the data in the block 2 column do not include the impacts of applying block one methodology, only the effects of applying block 2.

EPA did not establish emission rate goals for Vermont and the District of Columbia because they do not currently have affected EGUs.

End Notes

[1] 79 *Federal Register* 34830, "Carbon Pollution Emission Guidelines for Existing Stationary Sources: Electric Utility Generating Units," June 18, 2014 (hereinafter EPA Proposed Rule).

[2] 42 U.S.C. §7411(d).

[3] Vermont and the District of Columbia do not have emission rate goals, because they do not have electric generating units affected by the proposal in their jurisdictions.

[4] To satisfy the interim goal requirement, each state must demonstrate that the components of its plan would yield an emission rate that is less than or equal to the interim goal. In addition, EPA proposes that states provide annual performance updates to EPA during the interim period.

[5] See EPA, Goal Computation Technical Support Document, June 2012, at http://www2.epa.gov/carbon-

[6] For more details, see EPA, "Goal Computation Technical Support Document," June 2014, at http://www2.epa.gov/carbon

[7] EPA, Technical Support Document, *GHG Abatement Measures*, at http://www2.epa.gov/carbon-

[8] This generally equates to a 25 MW unit (25 MW * 8,760 hours = 219,000 MWh).

[9] This is measured on an annual basis for steam units and IGCC units and on a three-year rolling average basis for stationary combustion turbine units. For more information, the proposed rule references a discussion in the proposed rule for *new sources* at 79 *Federal Register* 1430 (January 8, 2014).

[10] CRS calculations using EPA's "Technical Support Document: Goal Computation-Appendix 7" Excel spreadsheet, at http://www2.epa.gov/carbon

[11] For the most part, energy generation refers to electricity, but some EGUs, namely combined heat and power facilities, also produce heat (referred to as "useful thermal output") that can be used on-site for other industrial processes.

[12] See EPA Proposed Rule, p. 34894.

[13] According to EPA, "IGCCs represent a very small sample size of three operating plants and have a different utilization pattern and different capital cost profile than NGCCs that result in a different set of redispatch economics. Likewise, high utilization [combustion turbines] that may be covered by the rule are generally less efficient and have higher emission rates than NGCCs, and are therefore generally less cost effective for redispatch purposes [i.e., building block 2]." See EPA, "Goal Computation Technical Support Document," June 2014, at http://www2.epa.gov/carbonpollution-standards/clean-power-plan-proposed-rule-technical-documents.

[14] CRS calculation based on 2012 data provided in EPA's technical document spreadsheets.

[15] At first glance, the numerator appears to have extraneous information. For example, it could simply contain pounds of CO2 from the various categories, instead of generation and emission rate data (which ultimately yields pounds).

[16] See EPA's Technical Support Document, *GHG Abatement Measures*.

[17] For states that use a greater portion of nuclear power as part of their electricity generation portfolio, adding this element to the denominator has a more pronounced effect. For example, South Carolina generated the highest percentage (53%) of its electricity generation from nuclear power in 2012. South Carolina's unadjusted emission rate decreased by 7% with the addition of at-risk nuclear power to the emission rate equation (CRS calculations,

using   EIA   electricity   generation,   by   source   and   state,   at
http://www.eia.gov/electricity/data.cfm#generation).

[18] For reasons discussed below, hydropower is not included in the 2012 renewable energy
baseline.

[19] See CRS Report R43572, *EPA's Proposed Greenhouse Gas Regulations for Existing Power
Plants: Frequently Asked Questions*, by James E. McCarthy et al.

[20] Heat rate is the efficiency of conversion from fuel energy input to electrical energy output often
expressed in terms of BTU per kiloWatt-hour.

[21]   EPA's   Technical   Support   Document,   *GHG   Abatement   Measures*,   at
http://www2.epa.gov/carbon-

[22] For a further discussion, see CRS Report R43621, *EPA's Proposed Greenhouse Gas
Regulations: Implications for the Electric Power Sector*, by Richard J. Campbell.

[23] For a further discussion, see CRS Report IN10089, *The Role of Natural Gas in EPA's
Proposed Clean Power Plan*, by Richard K. Lattanzio.

[24] EPA's Technical Support Document, *GHG Abatement Measures*.

[25] EPA's Technical Support Document, *GHG Abatement Measures*.

[26] If the state had NGCC under construction, this generating capacity would also be included.

[27] 11,202 MW * 8,784 hours (in 2012, a leap-year) * 0.7 = 68.9 million MWh.

[28] Unofficial proposed rule, p. 195.

[29] As of March 2013, 29 states (and the District of Columbia) have established renewable
portfolio standards (RPS), requiring retail electricity suppliers to supply a minimum
percentage or amount of their retail electricity load with electricity generated from eligible
sources of renewable energy, as defined by the state. An additional nine states have
voluntary goals. See the Database of State Incentives for Renewables and Efficiency, at
http://www.dsireusa.org/.

[30] Further details about this methodology are in a technical support document for the proposed
rule, *GHG Abatement Measures*, Chapter 4, at http://www2.epa.gov/carbon-

[31] According to EPA, " facilities are often excluded from RPS accounting. No states are expected
to develop any new large facilities.[32]

[32] EPA, Technical Support Document, Greenhouse Gas Abatement Measures, pp. 4-5.

[33] EPA, Technical Support Document, Greenhouse Gas Abatement Measures, pp. 4-5.

[34] The same MWh value is added to the denominator in both equations, having no impact on the
emission rate goals.

[35] EPA Proposed Rule, p. 34871.

[36] EPA, Technical Support Document, Greenhouse Gas Abatement Measures.

[37] EPA used data from EIA Form 861, which includes retail electricity sales and incremental
electricity savings from energy efficiency, available at http://www.eia.gov/electricity
/data/eia861/index.html.

[38] EPA, Technical Support Document, Greenhouse Gas Abatement Measures.

[39] EPA Proposed Rule, p. 34872.

[40] EPA generated these projections by using the 2012 retail sales data and average annual growth
rates for different regions provided in EIA's 2013 Annual Energy Outlook.

In: EPA's Proposed Carbon Dioxide Rule ...   ISBN: 978-1-63463-178-5
Editor: Carmella Ramos   © 2014 Nova Science Publishers, Inc.

Chapter 3

EPA'S PROPOSED GREENHOUSE GAS REGULATIONS FOR EXISTING POWER PLANTS: FREQUENTLY ASKED QUESTIONS[*]

James E. McCarthy, Robert Meltz, Jane A. Leggett, Jonathan L. Ramseur and Alissa M. Dolan

SUMMARY

Taking action to address climate change by reducing U.S. emissions of greenhouse gases (GHGs) is among President Obama's major goals. At an international conference in Copenhagen in 2009, he committed the United States to reducing emissions of greenhouse gases 17% by 2020, as compared to 2005 levels. At the time, 85 other nations also committed to reductions.

Since U.S. GHG emissions peaked in 2007, a variety of factors—some economic, some the effect of government policies at all levels—have brought the United States more than halfway to reaching the 2020 goal. Getting the rest of the way would likely depend, to some degree, on continued GHG emission reductions from electric power plants, which are the largest source of U.S. emissions.

---

[*] This is an edited, reformatted and augmented version of a Congressional Research Service publication, No. R43572, dated July 3, 2014.

In June 2013, the President released a Climate Action Plan that addressed this and other climate issues. At the same time, he directed the Environmental Protection Agency (EPA) to propose standards for "carbon pollution" (i.e., carbon dioxide, the principal GHG) from existing power plants by June 2014 and to finalize them in June 2015. Under the President's timetable, by June 2016, states would be required to submit to EPA plans to implement the standards.

On June 2, 2014, EPA responded to the first of these directives by releasing the proposed standards.

The proposal relies on authority given EPA by Congress decades ago in Section 111(d) of the Clean Air Act (CAA). This section has been little used—the last use was in 1996—and never interpreted by the courts, so a number of questions have arisen regarding the extent of EPA's authority and the mechanisms of implementation. EPA tends to refer to the regulations as "guideline documents"—although that term is not used in the statute—perhaps to indicate that the section is intended to give primary authority to the states. The proposed guideline document would set interim (2020s averages) and final (2030) emission rate goals for each state based on four "building blocks"—broad categories that describe different reduction measures; in general, however, the policies to be adopted to reach these goals would be determined by the states, not EPA.

EPA faced a number of issues in developing the proposed regulations:

- How large a reduction in emissions would it propose, and by when?
- What year would it choose as the base against which to measure progress?
- How flexible would it make the regulations? Would it adopt a "mass-based" limit on total emissions or a rate-based (e.g., pounds of carbon dioxide per megawatt-hour of electricity) approach?
- What role might allowance systems play in meeting the goals?
- Will compliance be determined only by the actions of power companies (i.e., "inside the fence" actions) or will actions by energy consumers ("outside the fence") be part of compliance strategies?
- Would states and power companies that have already reduced GHG emissions receive credit for doing so? What about states and power generators with high levels of emissions, perhaps due to heavy reliance on coal-fired power? Would they be required to reduce emissions more than others, less than others, or the same?
- What role would there be for existing programs at the state and regional levels, such as the Regional Greenhouse Gas Initiative

(RGGI), and for broader greenhouse gas reduction programs such as those implemented pursuant to California's AB 32?

This report summarizes EPA's proposal and answers many of these questions. In addition to discussing details of the proposed rule, the report addresses a number of questions regarding the reasons EPA is proposing this rule; EPA's authority under Section 111 of the CAA; EPA's previous experience using that authority; the steps the agency must take to finalize the proposed rule; and other background questions.

On June 2, 2014, the Environmental Protection Agency (EPA) released proposed standards for greenhouse gas (GHG) emissions from existing fossil-fueled power plants under Section 111(d) of the Clean Air Act.[1] The proposal appeared in the *Federal Register*, June 18, 2014.[2] The rule and various supporting materials are posted on EPA's website: http://www2.epa.gov /carbon-pollution-standards/clean-power-plan-proposed-rule.

Publication in the *Federal Register* began a public comment period, which will run until October 16, 2014. Comments can be submitted by Members and the public on http://www.regulations (docket number EPA-HQ-OAR-2013-0602). The agency will hold public hearings in Denver, Atlanta, Pittsburgh, and Washington, DC, during the week of July 28 in addition to allowing submission of written comments.

Prior to this rule's release, EPA had already conducted a significant amount of outreach to interested parties. According to Bloomberg BNA, "Senior Environmental Protection Agency officials consulted with at least 210 separate groups representing a broad range of interests in the Washington, DC, area and held more than 100 meetings and events with additional organizations across regional offices as the agency prepared its carbon pollution regulation for existing power plants."[3]

The proposal generated a substantial amount of interest even before its release, because the economy and the health, safety, and well-being of the nation depend on a reliable and affordable power supply. Congressional committees have asked EPA officials numerous questions about the rule, and individual Members have written EPA to express concerns regarding the rule's potential impacts.[4]

In order to provide basic information about EPA's pending action, this report addresses the proposal in a Q&A format.

BACKGROUND

Q: Why Is EPA Proposing This Rule?

A: EPA is proposing emissions guidelines to limit carbon dioxide (CO_2) emissions from existing power plants under Section 111(d) of the Clean Air Act (CAA) for a variety of reasons. Some important context includes the following:

- the Supreme Court in *Massachusetts v. EPA* in 2007 determined that "air pollutant," as used in the CAA, covers GHGs;[5]
- in December 2010, EPA entered into a settlement agreement to issue New Source Performance Standards for electric generating units (EGUs) under Section 111(b) of the CAA, which, in turn, prompts EPA's responsibilities under Section 111(d), covering existing EGUs;[6] and
- in the context of U.S. commitments under a 1992 international treaty, the United Nations Framework Convention on Climate Change (UNFCCC), President Obama pledged in 2009 to reduce U.S. GHG emissions by 17% below 2005 levels by 2020.[7]

Q: What Other Steps Has EPA Taken to Reduce GHG Emissions?

A: EPA has already promulgated GHG emission standards for light-duty and medium- and heavy-duty vehicles, using its authority under Section 202 of the CAA.[8] Light-duty vehicles (cars, SUVs, vans, and pickup trucks) and medium- and heavy-duty vehicles (including buses, heavy trucks of all kinds, and on-road work vehicles) are collectively the largest emitters of GHGs other than power plants. Together, on-road motor vehicles accounted for nearly 25% of U.S. GHG emissions in 2012.

Under the promulgated rules, standards for light-duty vehicles first took effect for Model Year (MY) 2012. Allowable GHG emissions will be gradually reduced each year from MY 2012 through MY 2025. In MY 2025, emissions from new vehicles must average about 50% less per mile than in MY 2010. The standards for heavier-duty vehicles began to take effect in MY 2014. They will require emission reductions of 6% to 23%, depending on the type of engine and vehicle, when fully implemented in MY 2018. A second round of standards, to address MY 2019 and later medium- and heavy-duty vehicles, is currently under development at EPA.[9]

EPA's position is that the promulgation of standards for motor vehicles also triggered Clean Air Act requirements that new major stationary sources of emissions (power plants, refineries, etc.) obtain permits for their GHG emissions, and install the Best Available Control Technology, as determined by state and EPA permit authorities on a case-by-case basis, prior to construction. The Supreme Court upheld that position on June 23, 2014, provided that the sources were already required to obtain permits for other conventional pollutants.[10]

The GHG permitting requirements for stationary sources have been in place since 2011, but have been limited by EPA's "Tailoring Rule" to the very largest emitters—fewer than 200 facilities, so far. The Court's June 23 decision invalidated the Tailoring Rule, but found that EPA could limit GHG permit requirements to "major" facilities, so-classified as a result of their emissions of conventional pollutants. In so doing, the Court limited the pool of potential GHG permittees to a number similar to what the Tailoring Rule would have provided.

Q: How Much Progress Has the United States Made in Reducing GHG Emissions?

A: The question of how much progress has been made depends on the base year chosen for comparison. In 2012, U.S. GHG emissions were 6,526 million metric tons (mmt) of CO_2- equivalent[11]—slightly less than 5% above 1990 emission levels. This is 10% below GHG emission levels in 2005, and more than halfway toward meeting President Obama's pledge to reduce U.S. GHG emissions to 17% below 2005 levels by 2020. U.S. GHG emissions peaked in 2007 at 7,325 mmt CO_2e.

As shown in **Figure 1**, during the period from 1990 to 2012, U.S. economic activity, measured as gross domestic product (GDP, adjusted for inflation), rose 73% while population increased 26%.

Q: How Much Does the Generation of Electricity Contribute to Total U.S. GHG Emissions?

Electricity generation accounted for about 31% of all U.S. GHG emissions in 2012. GHG emissions from electricity generation rose during 1990 to 2012 by 11%, while all other sources of GHG emissions grew by an average of 2%. GHG emissions from electricity generation in 2005 were 32% above 1990 levels, peaking in 2007 at 2,413 mmt CO_2e. In its 2014 Annual Energy Outlook, the U.S. Energy Information Administration (EIA) projected emissions from electricity generation to rise 3.6% from 2012 to 2020, assuming no further regulatory actions.[12] EIA's reference case projection would put electricity generation emissions at 12% below 2005 levels in 2020. Presumably, the EPA-proposed regulations for existing power plants will lower any future EIA projections.

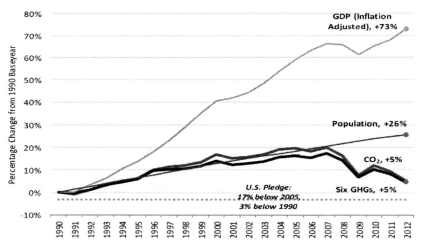

Source: CRS figure, using GHG emissions data from United States Environmental Protection Agency. *The U.S. Inventory of Greenhouse Gas Emissions and Sinks: 1990-2012,* EPA 430-14-003, April 15, 2014; and GDP and population data from U.S. Bureau of Economic Analysis, National Economic Accounts, "Table 7.1. Selected Per Capita Product and Income Series in Current and Chained Dollars," accessed May 27, 2014.

Note: GDP, or "gross domestic product," is one measure of national economic activity.

Figure 1. Percent Change in U.S. Greenhouse Gas (GHG) Emissions, the Economy, and Population.

STATUTORY AUTHORITY

Q: Under What Authority Is EPA Proposing These Regulations?

A: EPA's proposed regulations are required by CAA Section 111(d).[13] This provision calls on states to submit plans to EPA imposing "standards of performance" for pollutants emitted by *existing* stationary sources. The Section 111(d) mandate applies narrowly, however. It applies only when the pollutant (1) is neither covered by a National Ambient Air Quality Standard nor listed as a "hazardous air pollutant" under CAA Section 112,[14] and (2) would be regulated under a "new source performance standard" (NSPS) under Section 111(b) if the existing source were a *new* source. CO_2 already meets precondition (1).[15] CO_2 will meet precondition (2) once EPA's proposed NSPS for CO_2 emissions from fossil-fuel power plants are finalized, probably early next year.

The trigger that requires EPA to use Section 111(d) is Section 111(b). Section 111(b) requires EPA to issue NSPSs for any stationary source category on an EPA-maintained list of source categories that "cause[], or contribute[] significantly to, air pollution which may reasonably be anticipated to endanger public health or welfare." Once an NSPS is promulgated—to reiterate, for *new* sources in the source category—Section 111(d) is triggered for emissions of the same pollutant from *existing* sources in the source category, if the preconditions described above are met.[16] That is the basis for EPA's June 2 proposal. The intersection between these two rules is addressed below.

Q: How Is the Term "Standards of Performance," Required by Section 111(D), Defined in Statute and Case Law?

A: The act defines "standard of performance" as

> a standard for emissions of air pollutants which reflects the degree of emission limitation achievable through the application of the best system of emission reduction which (taking into account the cost of achieving such reduction and any nonair quality health and environmental impact and energy requirements) the Administrator determines has been adequately demonstrated.[17]

This definition makes clear that EPA's main task is to define the "best system of emission reduction," considering the indicated factors, on which the standard for emissions will be based. Most of the terms in the definition are themselves undefined in the act, leaving wide latitude for EPA interpretation.[18] This wide latitude is important in part because CAA Section 111 applies the phrase "standard of performance" to *both new and existing* facilities in the listed source category, yet is generally assumed to be more flexible and less stringent when applied to existing sources, reflecting implementation challenges in existing facilities compared to new ones. Supporting this assumption is that certain definition terms—such as "best," "taking into account cost," and "adequately demonstrated"—seem to accommodate comfortably the different technological and economic circumstances of existing facilities versus new ones. It should also be noted that Section 111(d) itself says that states may consider an existing facility's remaining useful life "among other factors."

Although all of the court interpretation of the CAA's definition of "standard of performance" stems from the phrase's use for *new* stationary sources, the cases arguably still shed light on how the definition might apply under Section 111(d) to the standards of performance that states are required to submit for *existing* sources. A full review of this case law is beyond the scope of this report. (EPA recently has offered its own, however.)[19] However, in light of ubiquitous claims that Section 111(d) affords EPA great flexibility as to what it may accept in state plans, it is worth keeping in mind that whatever states submit must, as Section 111(d) explicitly requires, include "standards of performance." That means that EPA's calculation of each state-specific emission-reduction goal must be based on measures that are "system[s] of emission reduction."[20] Whether some of the "building blocks" EPA proposed on June 2 as components of a system of emission reduction—such as boosting use of renewable fuels, reducing electricity demand, and investing in "smart grid" technology—constitute "systems of emission reduction" is not clear.

The shorthand for this flexibility issue that EPA faces is whether the state-specific emission-reduction goals EPA prescribes must be based solely on measures taken "inside the fence line" of specific plants, or whether "outside the fence line" measures can be considered part of a system of emission reduction.

Finally, the emission standards prescribed in EPA's June 2 proposal must be based on state approaches that are not only "system[s] of emission reduction," but also the "best" of such systems, considering the factors in the standard of performance definition.[21] Case law holds that EPA has "broad discretion" to weigh these factors.[22]

Q: When Has EPA Previously Used This Authority?

A: EPA has only promulgated rules under Section 111(d) a handful of times. Excluding guideline documents for incineration facilities, which rely in large part on a different section of the act, the *Code of Federal Regulations* contains only two Section 111(d) guideline documents.[23]

EPA's most recent attempt to use the authority was in the Clean Air Mercury Rule (CAMR, 2005), when EPA promulgated standards for mercury emissions from new power plants under Section 111(b) and set up a cap-and-trade system under Section 111(d) for existing power plants. In the final CAMR rule,[24] EPA apportioned a nationwide budget for mercury emissions among individual states. Each state was required to submit an implementation plan to EPA within 18 months of the rule's promulgation, detailing the controls it would impose on the coal-fired power plants within the state to meet the state's emissions budget. States could adopt EPA's emissions trading rule or choose to achieve the mandated reductions in some other way. If a state did neither, the cap-and-trade program outlined in CAMR was proposed as a Federal Implementation Plan (FIP). EPA set state-level budgets for a period beginning in 2010 (four and a half years after promulgation), and for a second period beginning in 2018.

The D.C. Circuit Court of Appeals vacated CAMR's 111(b) standards for new power plants in a 2008 decision,[25] so these 111(d) guidelines for existing power plants were never implemented. The court did not rule on whether the flexible approach taken by EPA for mercury controls (i.e., a cap-and-trade system) met the requirements of Section 111(d).

The most recent successful use of Section 111(d) came in 1996, when EPA used the authority to impose requirements on emissions of methane and non-methane organic compounds from landfills.[26] These regulations required the use of control equipment and set numeric emission limits for designated facilities (large landfills), with a compliance deadline of 30 months after the effective date of the state plan submitted to EPA. State plans were required to be submitted within nine months of promulgation of the Section 111(d) rule.

Q: Why Has Section 111(D) Been Infrequently Used?

A: As mentioned earlier, Section 111(d) can be used only for pollutants that are neither criteria pollutants (i.e., EPA has not set National Ambient Air Quality Standards for them under Section 109 of the act) nor hazardous air pollutants (HAPs), as identified in Section 112 of the act.[27] This is a relatively small number of pollutants. CO2, being neither a criteria pollutant nor a HAP, falls into that universe.[28]

Q: What Relationship Does This Proposal Have to EPA's January 2014 Proposal of GHG Standards for *New* Fossil-Fueled Power Plants?

A: EPA's January 2014 proposal for *new* fossil-fuel power plants was made under CAA Section 111(b). As discussed earlier, once EPA sets such a New Source Performance Standard under Section 111(b), Section 111(d) is triggered for existing sources in the same source category if the pollutant in question is neither covered by a NAAQS nor listed as a hazardous air pollutant.[29] CO2 satisfies this precondition, so EPA's January 2014 proposal for new power plants, once made final, will obligate the agency and the states to regulate CO2 emissions from *existing* fossil-fueled power plants.

Those likely to be regulated under Section 111(d) presumably are well aware of the 111(b)-111(d) linkage—no 111(b) NSPS means no 111(d) standards of performance for existing sources in the same category. Thus, even though the January 2014 proposal of NSPSs for new power plants will affect very few plants, it is nearly certain that once finalized, the rule will be vigorously challenged in court by utilities operating existing power plants potentially subject to the June 2 proposal under Section 111(d).

Q: Is the Rule Released on June 2 a Final Rule?

A: No. It is a proposed rule, on which EPA will take public comment. Under Section 307(d) of the CAA,[30] EPA is required to issue a proposed rule and hold a public comment period before issuing a final rule. The final rule may be changed from the proposal, so long as EPA provides an explanation in the *Federal Register* of the reasons for any major changes. At the least, when the agency promulgates a final version of the rule, it must provide a response to each of the significant comments, criticisms, and new data submitted during the proposed rule's public comment period.

THE PROPOSED RULE

Q: By How Much Would the Proposed Rule Reduce CO_2 Emissions?

A. EPA's proposed Section 111(d) rule does not set a future level of emissions from existing electricity generators. The proposal sets state goals for emission *rates*—as pounds of CO_2 emissions per megawatt-hour of electricity produced—not absolute emissions. It has been widely reported that the rule would require a 30% reduction in CO_2 emissions by 2030, compared to the level of emissions in 2005; but this is simply EPA's estimate of the rule's effect nationwide, not what the rule *requires*.

Effects on CO_2 emissions are calculated by computer models projecting the quantity of electricity produced by each state under the rule, multiplied by EPA's proposed state emission-rate goals. The actual emissions in the future will depend on how states choose to comply with the promulgated rule and how much electricity is generated (and at what generation units).

In 2012, CO_2 emissions from electricity generation were 2,023 million metric tons (mmt), or about 38% of total U.S. CO_2 emissions (excluding emissions and removals by land use and forestry).[31] EPA projects that the proposed Section 111(d) rule, Option 1—State Compliance, would reduce CO_2 emissions from electricity generation to 1,682 mmt when states reach their "final" emission rate goals in 2030. This would be an approximate absolute emissions reduction of 17% from 2012 levels, the base year for the proposed rule, and about 30% below the 2005 level of CO_2 emissions from U.S. electricity generation.[32] EPA's modeling of the rule also estimates interim reductions, as illustrated in **Figure 2**.

The 2030 "final goals" for states' emissions rates would continue as long as the rule remains in place. As **Figure 2** illustrates, absolute CO_2 emissions from electricity generation would likely increase after 2030 at the rate of growth of electricity production (unless very low- or no-emitting fuels make going beyond the emissions rate standard economically attractive).

Q: Did EPA Propose More Than One Option for the Standards?

A: EPA proposed only one set of emission rate standards (labeled Option 1 in the proposal), but it asked for comment on an alternative set (labeled Option 2) in which the final state goals would be less stringent and would have to be attained more quickly—by 2025, five years earlier than under Option 1.

Besides offering an alternative option for comment, the agency also identified two ways in which states could comply with either the proposed standards or the alternative: a State Compliance Approach or a Regional Compliance Approach. The goals would be the same for the two compliance approaches. Under the State Compliance Approach, each state would pursue its goal on its own—as is typically the case in CAA State Implementation Plans. However, under the Regional Approach, states voluntarily could join with other states to implement multistate compliance approaches (e.g., maintaining the nine-state cap-and-trade system under the Regional Greenhouse Gas Initiative). Under the Regional Compliance Approach, states would have additional time to submit implementation plans, and the costs and benefits of compliance are estimated by EPA to be somewhat lower than under the State Compliance Approach.

Because it serves as the base of EPA's proposal, in the remainder of this report, we generally focus on the Option 1—State Compliance Approach.

Q: What Is the Range of State Emission-Rate Goals?

A: The proposal sets interim emission-rate goals for each state for the period from 2020 to 2029 and a final goal for 2030. The proposed 2030 goals range from 215 pounds of CO_2 per megawatt-hour in Washington State to 1,783 pounds in North Dakota. In general, states that rely on coal for a high percentage of their total power generation would be allowed higher emission rates than states that rely more heavily on natural gas, nuclear, and renewable power. **Table 1** shows the final (2030) goals for each state ranked from highest average emissions allowed to lowest.

The data presented here are based on the agency's proposed approach. The agency also asked for comment on an alternative option that would shorten the compliance period from 10 years to 5 (i.e., a final goal reached in 2025), with a less stringent set of CO2 emission rates. Under both the proposed and alternative options, the agency also proposes to allow submission of multistate plans, the effects of which might differ slightly from the single-state approach.

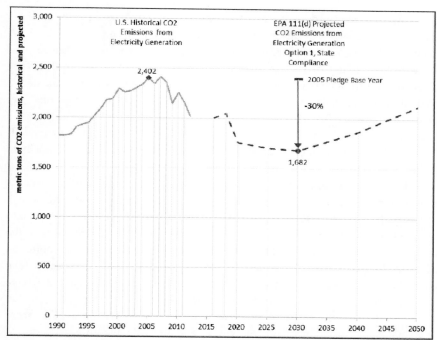

Source: CRS figure from U.S. Environmental Protection Agency, *The U.S. Inventory of Greenhouse Gas Emissions and Sinks: 1990-2012*, Washington, DC: 2014; and EPA spreadsheet "Illustrative State compliance scenario for Option 1," available at http://www.epa.gov/airmarkets/powersectormodeling/cleanpowerplan.html.

Note: EPA-projected emissions converted from short tons to metric tons by CRS.

Figure 2. U.S. CO2 Emissions from Electricity Generation, Historical and Projected.

Q: How Did EPA Establish the State-Level Goals in the Proposed Rule?

A: EPA describes the rule as having four "building blocks," which were used to generate state-specific emission rate goals. The first of these calls for "heat-rate" (i.e., efficiency) improvements at coal-fired power plants (i.e., reductions in the amount of heat, as measured in Btu's, necessary to generate a megawatt-hour of electricity). Since CO_2 emissions are directly related to the amount of coal burned, a reduction in the heat rate of a given percentage would lead to a reduction in CO_2 emissions of the same percentage. For each state's coal-fired power plants, the agency began by determining an average

CO_2 emission rate (in pounds of CO_2 per megawatt-hour), using data for 2012. Based on its review of relevant engineering studies and emissions data, EPA determined that coal-fired plants could reasonably be expected to reduce their average heat rate by 6%, so the agency reduced each state's 2012 CO_2 emission rate from coal-fired units by that percentage. For example, if a state's coal-fired power plants averaged 2,000 pounds of CO_2 emissions per megawatt-hour in 2012, the first building block would lower the state's average emission rate for those coal-fired units to 1,880 pounds per megawatt-hour. A decreased average rate at a state's coal-fired units would contribute toward a decrease in the state's overall emission rate.

The second building block is based on "dispatch changes" among a state's electric generating units (EGUs). As demand for power rises over the course of a day, the system operator or regional transmission organization calls into service ("dispatches") additional generating units. As demand decreases in the evening, these additional units are taken off-line. The same principle applies as demand fluctuates over the course of a year. Because coal-fired plants take hours or days to ramp up to their design capacity, and because they have traditionally been cheaper to operate than most other sources, they have tended to be dispatched before natural-gas-fired units. In the last five years, this order of dispatch has been changing, however, and the rule would set a goal of increasing the dispatch of natural-gas-combined-cycle (NGCC) plants, which have lower CO_2 emissions per megawatt-hour generated, in place of higher emission coal- and oil-fired power.[33] The agency estimated that, in aggregate, NGCC units utilized about 46% of their total generating capacity in 2012. EPA determined that this NGCC capacity use could be increased to 70%. For goal-setting purposes, the second building block assumes that a state's NGCC plants will, in aggregate, use up to 70% of their capacity, rather than the current averages, which range from 1% in South Dakota to 63% in Connecticut. The additional NGCC power is assumed to replace a portion of the state's coal-fired and other higher CO_2 emitting sources, thus reducing the rate of CO_2 emissions per megawatt-hour generated.

The third building block assumes the use of additional low- or no-carbon emitting power sources, principally renewable energy. To estimate how much power could be expected to come from renewable sources, EPA grouped the states into six regions and developed state-specific goals based on the average of existing renewable portfolio standards[34] applicable in 2020 in each region. The agency used these averages to compute regional growth factors for renewable electricity, which it applied to each state's initial (2012) renewable energy generation level. This additional electricity from zero-emission energy sources lowers the states' CO_2 emission rates. A similar adjustment was made for under-construction and "at-risk" nuclear power units.[35]

Table 1. State CO2 Emission Performance Goals, 2030
(lbs. of CO2 emitted per net megawatt-hour of electricity generated)

State	2030 State Goal
North Dakota	1,783
Montana	1,771
Kentucky	1,763
Wyoming	1,714
West Virginia	1,620
Missouri	1,544
Indiana	1,531
Kansas	1,499
Nebraska	1,479
Ohio	1,338
Utah	1,322
Hawaii	1,306
Iowa	1,301
Illinois	1,271
Wisconsin	1,203
Maryland	1,187
Tennessee	1,163
Michigan	1,161
Colorado	1,108
Alabama	1,059
Pennsylvania	1,052
New Mexico	1,048
Alaska	1,003
North Carolina	992
Arkansas	910
Oklahoma	895
Louisiana	883
Minnesota	873
Delaware	841
Georgia	834
Virginia	810
Texas	791
Rhode Island	782
South Carolina	772

Table 1. (Continued)

State	2030 State Goal
South Dakota	741
Florida	740
Arizona	702
Mississippi	692
Nevada	647
Massachusetts	576
New York	549
Connecticut	540
California	537
New Jersey	531
New Hampshire	486
Maine	378
Oregon	372
Idaho	228
Washington	215

Source: U.S. EPA.

Notes: Because Vermont and the District of Columbia lack affected sources, no goals were proposed for these jurisdictions. In addition, no goals were proposed for Indian country or for U.S. territories. The agency does plan to establish goals for areas of Indian country and possibly for some U.S. territories in the future. EPA requested comment on how it should proceed in these cases.

The fourth building block reduces the emissions rate by including demand-side energy efficiency programs. Although some states currently have more stringent energy efficiency requirements than others, EPA assumes that by 2030, all states can implement such programs, with roughly similar results. These programs are assumed to reduce power demand by roughly 9% to 12% in each state by 2030.

For an example of how these building blocks were used to produce a state emission-rate goal, see EPA's "Goal Computation Technical Support Document" at http://www2.epa.gov/sites/ production/files/2014-05/documents /20140602tsd-goal-computation.pdf.

Q: Would States and Companies That Have Already Reduced GHG Emissions Receive Credit for Doing So?

A: States do not receive "credit" in their goals for emission reduction measures already taken. Whether individual power companies will receive credit will be decided by states as they develop their implementation plans. The rule requires each state to submit an implementation plan to EPA that identifies what measures/regulations the state will implement to reach its goal.

At the same time, a few states with high percentages of renewable power in their total power supply do effectively receive credit for the levels of renewable power already achieved, because a state's interim and final emission rate goals are based in part on the amount of renewable power expected in the *region* to which it belongs. If a state's current renewable generation percentage exceeds its regional percentage target, EPA's goal calculation methodology assumes the state would adjust its renewable energy generation to match the regional target. For example, Iowa, South Dakota, Minnesota, and Maine all have renewable energy goals calculated by EPA that are lower than their 2012 generation levels. Assuming these states continue to use renewable energy at their 2012 levels, the renewable energy building block would effectively give them credit for early action.

Q: How Does EPA's Proposed Rule Interact with Existing GHG Emission Reduction Programs in the States, Namely the Regional Greenhouse Gas Initiative and California's Cap-and-Trade System?

A number of U.S. states have taken action requiring greenhouse gas (GHG) emission reductions. The most aggressive actions have come from a coalition of states from the Northeast and Mid-Atlantic regions—the Regional Greenhouse Gas Initiative[36]—and California.[37] The Regional Greenhouse Gas Initiative (RGGI) is a cap-and-trade system involving nine states that took effect in 2009.[38] RGGI applies to CO_2 emissions from electric power plants with capacities to generate 25 megawatts or more.

Pursuant to legislation passed in 2006, California established a cap-and-trade program that took effect in 2013. California's cap covers multiple GHGs and when fully implemented in 2015, will apply to multiple sectors, covering approximately 85% of California's GHG emissions. Although EPA's proposed rule measures state compliance in terms of a CO_2 emissions rate, EPA allows states considerable flexibility in terms of meeting its emissions rate goals. For example, EPA's new regulations would allow states to meet their CO_2 emissions rate goals using mass-based reduction programs, such as cap-and-trade systems. States can establish new programs to meet their goals or use existing programs and regulations. Moreover, states can meet their goals individually or collaborate with other states to create (or use existing) multistate plans. EPA provides states with additional time to submit their plans if states decide to combine their efforts.

EPA used 2012 data to prepare each state's emission rate goals. The proposed rule does not have a process for providing credit for emissions reductions made prior to 2012. However, EPA points out that states that began action prior to 2012, including a shift to less carbon-intensive energy sources or energy efficiency improvements, will be "better positioned" to meet state-specific emission rate goals.[39]

Q: What Role Is There for "Outside-the-Fence" Emission Reductions?

A: Because the states will decide how to reduce emission rates to reach the EPA-set goals, this question is not directly answered in the proposed rule. In setting the goals for each state, however, EPA clearly anticipated that some reductions will come from actions taken by actors other than power companies or specific EGUs (actions that have been referred to as "outside-the-fence" reductions). One of the four building blocks of the proposed rule is the application of demand-side energy efficiency measures, such as the installation of more efficient lighting products, better insulation, and more efficient electric appliances. In the Preamble to the proposed rule, EPA states its intention to establish a "toolbox of decision support resources" for the states, which will include outside-the-fence measures such as energy efficiency and renewable energy policies and programs.[40]

NEXT STEPS

Q: What Are the Next Steps? How Will EPA Finalize This Rule?

A: On June 2, EPA made the rule and various supporting materials available on its website. The rule appeared in the *Federal Register* (FR) June

18. Publication in the FR began the formal comment period, which will run 120 days. As noted earlier, EPA plans four public hearings during the week of July 28 (in Atlanta, Denver, Pittsburgh, and Washington, DC), as well as taking written comments on the regulations website.[41]

After the close of the comment period, EPA will consider the comments it received, revise the rule to the extent it determines that to be appropriate, and prepare additional supporting materials. Then, upon completion of its internal consideration, the agency will forward a draft final rule to the Office of Information and Regulatory Affairs (OIRA) at the White House Office of Management and Budget.

Q: What Role Does OIRA (I.E., the White House) Play in Developing the Final Rule?

A: OIRA/interagency review is a normal part of the rulemaking process for most federal agencies. Under Executive Order (E.O.) 12866, OIRA oversees an interagency review process; it also generally conducts meetings with principal stakeholders. These meetings are known as "12866 meetings," and OIRA posts information about them on its website.[42]

This interagency review process sometimes results in significant changes to a rule. At the least, OIRA will seek to ensure that EPA has developed a rule that addresses concerns raised during the comment period, that the rule is supported by the agency's Regulatory Impact Analysis[43] and any other accompanying analyses, that the rule is legally defensible, and that the rule is consistent with the President's policy priorities.

Under E.O. 12866, OIRA reviews are to be completed within 90 days of a rule's submission by the regulatory agency, but often they extend for longer periods.[44] This rule is not likely to languish at OIRA, however. In directing EPA to develop the rule, in June 2013, the President established a schedule for promulgation and implementation, directing EPA to promulgate a final rule by June 1, 2015. Given the high priority placed on this rule by the President, both EPA and OIRA are likely to make every effort to adhere to that schedule.

E.O. 12866 requires both regulatory agencies and OIRA to disclose certain information about how OIRA's regulatory reviews are conducted. Specifically, agencies are required to identify for the public (1) the substantive changes made to rules between the draft submitted to OIRA for review and the action subsequently announced and (2) changes made at the suggestion or recommendation of OIRA. OIRA is required to provide agencies with a copy of all written communications between OIRA personnel and parties outside of the executive branch, and a list of the dates and names of individuals involved in substantive oral communications.

After the completion of review, the EPA Administrator will sign the final rule and send it to the *Federal Register* for promulgation.[45]

Q: When Will the Final Rule Take Effect, and How Will It Be Implemented?

A: Once finalized, major rules generally may take effect no sooner than 60 days after publication in the *Federal Register*.[46] Assuming that the final rule is signed June 1, 2015, it would likely be effective sometime in the summer of 2015. According to the schedule announced by the President, the states would then have until June 30, 2016, to submit plans detailing how they will implement its provisions.

EPA has proposed some modifications to the schedule for the state plan submissions, however. Under the proposed rule, states will be allowed to request an additional year for submission of a complete plan, provided that they have taken "meaningful steps" toward completion by the 2016 deadline. States choosing to participate in a multistate plan would have until June 30, 2018, to submit the plan.

Q: What Happens if a State Fails to Submit an Adequate Plan by the Appropriate Deadline?

A: EPA cannot compel a state to submit a Section 111(d) plan. Rather, should a state fail to submit a satisfactory plan by EPA's deadline, CAA Section 111(d) authorizes EPA to prescribe a plan for the state. This authority is the same, Section 111(d) says, as EPA's authority to prescribe federal implementation plans (FIPs) when a state fails to submit a state implementation plan to achieve a NAAQS.[47] Questions have been raised as to whether EPA has the authority to include in its EPA-promulgated plans all the measures, such as demand-side energy efficiency requirements, that states may include in their 111(d) plans.

COSTS AND BENEFITS OF THE RULE

Q: What Role Will Cost Play in EPA's Choice of Emission Standards?

A: Under Section 111(a)(1)'s definition of "standards of performance," EPA must consider cost in developing the regulations. In addition, Section 111(d)(1) states, "Regulations of the Administrator under this paragraph shall permit the State in applying a standard of performance to any particular source under a plan submitted under this paragraph to take into consideration, among other factors, the remaining useful life of the existing source to which such standard applies."

EPA's regulations implementing this language (40 C.F.R. 60.22(b)), which were promulgated in 1975 and 1989, provide additional detail:

(b) Guideline documents published [by EPA] under this section will provide information for the development of State plans, such as:

(1) Information concerning known or suspected endangerment of public health or welfare caused, or contributed to, by the designated pollutant.

(2) A description of systems of emission reduction which, in the judgment of the Administrator, have been adequately demonstrated.

(3) Information on the degree of emission reduction which is achievable with each system, together with information on the costs and environmental effects of applying each system to designated facilities.

(4) Incremental periods of time normally expected to be necessary for the design, installation, and startup of identified control systems.

(5) An emission guideline that reflects the application of the best system of emission reduction (considering the cost of such reduction) that has been adequately demonstrated for designated facilities, and the time within which compliance with emission standards of equivalent stringency can be achieved. The Administrator will specify different emission guidelines or compliance times or both for different sizes, types, and classes of designated facilities when costs of control, physical limitations, geographical location, or similar factors make subcategorization appropriate.

(6) Such other available information as the Administrator determines may contribute to the formulation of State plans.

Q: What Are EPA's Estimates of the Costs of This Rule?

A: EPA estimates the cost of the proposed rule at $7.3 billion to $8.8 billion annually in 2030. Because states will determine how to comply with the goals established by the final rule, EPA refers to these cost estimates as "illustrative" and notes that they "do not represent the full suite of compliance flexibilities states may ultimately pursue."[48] EPA describes the cost estimate as including "the net change in the annualized cost of capital investment in new generating sources and heat rate improvements at coal steam facilities, the change in the ongoing costs of operating pollution controls, shifts between or amongst various fuels, demand-side energy efficiency measures, and other actions associated with compliance."[49]

Although the rule may impose $7.3 billion to $8.8 billion in annual control costs by 2030, EPA estimates that the average monthly residential electricity bill will decline by 9% in 2030, as consumption of electricity declines due to efficiency measures.[50]

Q: What Are the Benefits EPA Estimates for the Proposed Section 111(D) Rule?

A: In the Preamble to the proposed rule, EPA cites monetized CO_2-reduction benefits of the rule to be $30 billion in 2030 (in 2011 dollars) and the health-related co-benefits of the rule to be an additional $23 billion to $59 billion.[51]

In the accompanying Regulatory Impact Analysis, the agency provides additional detail, including ranges of benefits based on a variety of assumptions. EPA's estimates for Option 1— State Compliance, in the Regulatory Impact Analysis range from $22 billion to $88 billion in 2020, rising to $36 billion to $150 billion in 2030.[52] These estimates include benefits of slowing climate change, as well as avoiding premature deaths and illnesses from other air pollution. With estimated compliance costs of about $7.5 billion in 2020 rising to a maximum of $8.8 billion in 2030, EPA expects that its Section 111(d) proposal would yield net benefits of $26 billion to $50 billion in 2020, rising to $49 billion to $84 billion in 2030.[53]

EPA expects its Section 111(d) proposal to avoid some degree of greenhouse gas-induced climate change, by directly reducing CO_2 (the major human-related greenhouse gas), and by reducing atmospheric concentrations of ozone, particulate matter, and other pollutants, all of which also influence climate change. EPA estimates the benefits of reducing CO_2 emissions (i.e., the climate benefits, excluding the health-related co-benefits) to range from $5 billion to $52 billion in 2020, rising to a range of $10 billion to $94 billion in 2030. The benefits of slowing climate change are about 13% to 76% of the total monetized benefits of the proposed rule, depending on the assumptions selected.

EPA calculated the benefits of avoided climate change by multiplying tons of CO_2 emission reductions in each year by corresponding ranges of "social costs of carbon" (SCC) in that year. The SCC is an estimate of the avoided costs of future climate change per ton of CO_2 avoided. EPA uses the ranges of values published by an Interagency Working Group on the Social Costs of Carbon in November 2013.[54] Stakeholders have critiqued these SCC estimates, with some arguing the range should be lower and others higher.

EPA expects that the 111(d) proposal simultaneously will reduce other air pollutants, avoid premature deaths and illnesses, and reduce material damages. Under most assumptions, the majority of monetized benefits EPA estimated for its proposal come from reductions, or "co-benefits" of pollutants other than CO_2. EPA valued the co-benefits of its Section 111(d) proposal at $24 billion to $62 billion in 2030.

EPA did not quantify other expected co-benefits of this rule, including reduced exposures to several hazardous air pollutants (such as mercury and hydrogen chloride), carbon monoxide, and reduced direct exposures to sulfur dioxide (SO_2) and nitrogen oxides (NOx). EPA also did not quantify pollution effects on ecosystems or visibility.

Q: Under Section 111(D), Are the Benefits of the Rule Required to Exceed Its Cost?

A: Section 111(d) does not impose a cost-benefit test. E.O. 12866, however, states that "in choosing among alternative regulatory approaches, agencies should select those approaches that maximize net benefits (including potential economic, environmental, public health and safety, and other advantages; distributive impacts; and equity), unless a statute requires another regulatory approach."[55]

CONGRESSIONAL REVIEW

Q: Does the Congressional Review Act apply to the Proposed Rule?

The Congressional Review Act (CRA) provides a mechanism by which Congress may review and disapprove of agency rules through passage of a joint resolution that is eligible for expedited procedures in the Senate.[56] If passed by both houses of Congress, such a joint resolution would be sent to the President for his signature or veto.

It does not appear that the CRA applies to *proposed* rules issued by an agency. Arguably a proposed rule does not satisfy the CRA definition of a "rule."[57] A proposed rule is not "designed to implement, interpret, or prescribe law or policy";[58] instead, it is generally created by the agency as a draft with which to solicit and receive public comments.[59] Additionally, arguably a proposed rule has no "future effect" because a proposed rule may not go into effect until comments are received and considered by the agency and a final rule is published in the *Federal Register*.[60]

The Government Accountability Office (GAO) specifically advises agencies not to submit proposed rules to Congress or GAO under the CRA.[61] In 2014, Senator Mitch McConnell requested[62] that GAO analyze Congress's authority to consider a CRA resolution disapproving of EPA's proposed rule entitled "Standards of Performance for Greenhouse Gas Emissions from New Stationary Sources: Electric Utility Generating Unit."[63] In his letter, Senator McConnell argued that this proposed rule was different from other proposed rules because a provision of the CAA "gives immediate legal effect to the notice of proposed rulemaking."[64] In its response, GAO limited its analysis to three questions regarding GAO's role in the CRA and its precedents analyzing whether specific agency actions are rules under the CRA.[65] It concluded that "the terms of [the] CRA, and its supporting legislative history, clearly do not provide a role for GAO with regard to proposed rules, and do not require agencies to submit proposed rules to GAO."[66]

Furthermore, it stated that prior GAO decisions found "that an agency action constituted a rule for CRA purposes ... [if] the action imposed requirements that were both certain and final."[67] Since proposed rules "are proposals for future agency action that are subject to change ... and do not have a binding effect on the obligations of any party,"[68] GAO concluded they are "not a triggering event for CRA purposes."[69] However, GAO also noted that because the CRA's expedited procedure for review of agency rules was enacted pursuant to Congress's constitutional authority to establish its own procedural rules,[70] it is for "Congress to decide whether [the] CRA would apply to a resolution disapproving a proposed rule."[71]

End Notes

[1] 42 U.S.C. §7411(d).

[2] U.S. EPA, "Carbon Pollution Emission Guidelines for Existing Stationary Sources: Electric Utility Generating Units," Proposed Rule, 79 *Federal Register* 34830, June 18, 2014.

[3] "EPA Consulted with Hundreds of Groups on Carbon Rule for Existing Power Plants," *Daily Environment Report*, April 8, 2014. For EPA's discussion of the pre-proposal outreach effort, see Section III of the Preamble to the proposed rule, "Stakeholder Outreach and Conclusions," 79 *Federal Register* 34845-34851.

[4] See, for example, the letter from a bipartisan group of 47 Senators to EPA Administrator Gina McCarthy, May 22, 2014, at http://www.fischer.senate.gov/public/_cache/files/79d2321e-175c-4456-b4c7-f9b600e15288/5.22.14-senateghg-dear-colleague-letter.pdf.

[5] Massachusetts v. EPA, 549 U.S. 497 (2007), actually involved GHG emissions from motor vehicles, not power plants. In 2011, however, the Court explicitly ruled that "air pollutant" includes GHGs when applied to power plants under Section 111. American Elec. Power Co., Inc. v. Connecticut, 131 S. Ct. 2527, 2537-38 (2011).

[6] See CRS Report R41103, *Federal Agency Actions Following the Supreme Court's Climate Change Decision in Massachusetts v. EPA: A Chronology*, by Robert Meltz, p. 6.

[7] See CRS Report R40001, *A U.S.-Centric Chronology of the United Nations Framework Convention on Climate Change*, by Jane A. Leggett; and CRS Report R43120, *President Obama's Climate Action Plan*, coordinated by Jane A. Leggett.

[8] See CRS Report R40506, *Cars, Trucks, and Climate: EPA Regulation of Greenhouse Gases from Mobile Sources*, by James E. McCarthy and Brent D. Yacobucci, and CRS Report R42721, *Automobile and Truck Fuel Economy (CAFE) and Greenhouse Gas Standards*, by Brent D. Yacobucci, Bill Canis, and Richard K. Lattanzio.

[9] For additional information on these requirements, see CRS Report R40506, *Cars, Trucks, and Climate: EPA Regulation of Greenhouse Gases from Mobile Sources*, by James E. McCarthy and Brent D. Yacobucci.

[10] Utility Air Regulatory Group v. Environmental Protection Agency, No. 12-1146, 2014 Westlaw 2807314 (U.S. June 23, 2014).

[11] CO_2-equivalents (CO_2e) result from weighting the mass of emissions of a GHG (e.g., methane, sulfur hexafluoride, etc.) by its effect, relative to the effect of CO2, on radiative forcing of the climate system over a specified time period (usually 100 years). Using this method, gases of different atmospheric lifetimes and potencies can be compared or added. Various assumptions affect the relative warming potential of different GHG compounds.

[12] U.S. Energy Information Administration (EIA), "Annual Energy Outlook 2014," Table 18. Carbon Dioxide Emissions by Sector and Source, May 7, 2014, http://www.eia.gov/forecasts/aeo/tables_ref.cfm.

[13] 42 U.S.C. §7411(d).

[14] The CAA regulates emissions from stationary sources in multiple ways, three of which are relevant here. The first way is by National Ambient Air Quality Standards, reserved for

harmful but not extremely hazardous pollutants from "numerous or diverse mobile or stationary sources." CAA §108(a)(1)(B); 42 U.S.C. §7408(a)(1)(B). NAAQSs are implemented by source-specific emission limits imposed by states in "state implementation plans." CAA §110; 42 U.S.C. §7410. The second way is by federally prescribed national emission standards for hazardous air pollutants, that is, particularly harmful pollutants. CAA §112; 42 U.S.C. §7412. And the third, of interest here, is by federally prescribed standards of performance for new stationary sources. CAA §111; 42 U.S.C. §7411.

[15] There is an alternate reading of this precondition, owing to the fact that in the 1990 amendments to the CAA, inconsistent House and Senate amendments to Section 111(d) were enacted. Under the House amendment, Section 111(d) standards of performance are barred for air pollutants "emitted from a *source category* ... regulated under Section 112" (emphasis added), the section covering hazardous air pollutants. Because fossil-fuel power plants are indeed a source category regulated under Section 112, this argument concludes that Section 111(d) does not allow EPA to restrict GHG emissions from existing such plants. The Senate amendment, on the other hand, places off limits only *air pollutants*, rather than source categories, regulated under Section 112. GHGs are not regulated under Section 112, so the Senate amendment poses no obstacle to EPA's June 2 proposal. EPA's Legal Memorandum accompanying the June 2 proposed regulations provides an extended explanation of why the agency follows the Senate amendment.

[16] See, e.g., American Elec. Power Co., Inc. v. Connecticut, 131 S. Ct. 2527, 2537 (2011).

[17] CAA §111(a)(1); 42 U.S.C. §7411(a)(1).

[18] The term "air pollutant" *is* defined in CAA Section 302 and, important here, has been held by the Supreme Court, with specific reference to Section 111, to include GHGs. *American Elec. Power*, 131 S. Ct. at 2537.

[19] EPA's legal interpretation of "standard of performance" can be found in three places: (1) the preamble to the agency's proposed rule for new power plants: Standards of Performance for Greenhouse Gas Emissions from New Stationary Sources: Electric Utility Generating Units, 79 Fed. Reg. 1430, 1462-1467 (January 8, 2014); (2) the preamble to the June 2 proposed rule; and (3) an EPA-prepared Legal Memorandum accompanying the June 2 proposed rule, available at http://www2.epa.gov/carbon-. See, e.g., Essex Chemical Corp. v. Ruckelshaus, 486 F. 2d 427, 433 (D.C. Cir. 1973) (to be "adequately demonstrated," the "system of emission reduction" must be "reasonably reliable, reasonably efficient, and reasonably expected to serve the interests of pollution control without becoming exorbitantly costly in an economic and environmental way").

[20] 42 U.S.C. §7411(a)(1).

[21] *Id.*

[22] Sierra Club v. Costle, 657 F.2d 298, 321 (D.C. Cir. 1981). *Accord*, Lignite Energy Council v. U.S. EPA, 198 F.3d 930, 933 (D.C. Cir. 1999).

[23] The two guideline documents in the C.F.R. are "Emission Guidelines and Compliance Times for Municipal Solid Waste Landfills," at 40 C.F.R. 60.30c, and "Emission Guidelines and Compliance Times for Sulfuric Acid Production Units," at 40 C.F.R. 60.30d. EPA also appears to have issued four guideline documents that do not appear in the C.F.R.

[24] U.S. EPA, Standards of Performance for New and Existing Stationary Sources: Electric Utility Steam Generating Units, Final Rule, 70 *Federal Register* 28606, May 18, 2005.

[25] New Jersey v. EPA, 517 F.3d 574 (D.C. Cir. 2008). The court found that EPA was obligated to promulgate standards for mercury and other hazardous air pollutants under Section 112 of the act, and therefore vacated the NSPS under Section 111(b).

[26] U.S. EPA, Standards of Performance for New Stationary Sources and Guidelines for Control of Existing Sources: Municipal Solid Waste Landfills, Final Rule, 61 *Federal Register* 9905, March 12, 1996.

[27] But see note 15 above.

[28] See also the first question under "Statutory Authority," above.

[29] However, see note 15 above.

[30] 42 U.S.C. §7607(d).

[31] U.S. Environmental Protection Agency, *The U.S. Inventory of Greenhouse Gas Emissions and Sinks: 1990-2012*, Washington, DC: 2014.

[32] The base year for the proposed rule is 2012, although some have reported it as 2005. The comparison with emissions in 2005 may be relevant because of President Obama's pledge in 2009 to reduce total U.S. GHG emissions 17% below the 2005 level by 2020.

[33] According to EPA, NGCC units can produce as much as 46% more electricity from a given input of Btu's than coal-fired steam EGUs.

[34] Renewable portfolio standards, adopted by about 29 states and the District of Columbia (as of March 2013), require retail electricity suppliers to supply a minimum percentage or amount of their retail electricity load with electricity generated from eligible sources of renewable energy, as defined by the state. For additional information, see the Database of State Incentives for Renewables and Efficiency, at http://www.dsireusa.org/.

[35] EPA identified five nuclear units under construction in Georgia, South Carolina, and Tennessee, and 5.7 gigawatts of nuclear units (about 6% of the nation's nuclear capacity) at risk of retirement.

[36] See CRS Report R41836, *The Regional Greenhouse Gas Initiative: Lessons Learned and Issues for Policymakers*, by Jonathan L. Ramseur.

[37] In addition, EPA states that 38 states have renewable portfolio standards or goals, and utilities in 47 states have demand-side energy efficiency programs. See Preamble to the proposed rule, at 79 *Federal Register* 34835.

[38] Connecticut, Delaware, Maine, Maryland, Massachusetts, New Hampshire, New York, Rhode Island, and Vermont. New Jersey participated in the program from 2009 through the end of 2011.

[39] 79 *Federal Register* 34918.

[40] Ibid., p. 34928.

[41] The written submissions, transcripts of any public hearings, and all EPA supporting documents are available to the public in a regulatory docket at http://www.regulations. The docket number for this rule is EPA-HQ-OAR-2013- 0602.

[42] See http://www.reginfo.gov.

[43] Regulatory Impact Analyses, required under Executive Order 12866, provide an agency's analysis of the expected costs and benefits of a rule. See additional discussion under "Costs and Benefits of the Rule," below.

[44] Executive Order 12866, "Regulatory Planning and Review," 58 Federal Register 51735, October 4, 1993. For an electronic copy of this executive order, see http://www.whitehouse.gov/omb/inforeg/eo12866.pdf.

[45] For additional discussion of OIRA's role in the federal rulemaking process, see CRS Report RL32397, *Federal Rulemaking: The Role of the Office of Information and Regulatory Affairs*, coordinated by Maeve P. Carey.

[46] 5 U.S.C. §801(a)(3)(A).

[47] CAA §110(c); 42 U.S.C. §7410(c).

[48] EPA, Regulatory Impact Analysis for the Proposed Carbon Pollution Guidelines for Existing Power Plants and Emission Standards for Modified and Reconstructed Power Plants, June 2014, p. ES-7, at http://www2.epa.gov/sites/production/files/2014-06/documents /20140602ria-clean-power-plan.pdf.

[49] Ibid., p. ES-8 (footnote omitted).

[50] Preamble to the proposed rule at 79 *Federal Register* 34934.

[51] This estimate is for Option 1—Regional Compliance, using a 3% discount rate, which reflects the preference of most people to have money now rather than in the future. 79 *Federal Register* 34839.

[52] All in 2011 dollars. These estimates are for EPA's Option 1 proposal with state compliance, on which CRS focuses as it best reflects the rule as proposed by EPA. Benefits for Option 2 and/or regional compliance would be slightly lower, particularly because EPA estimates that the regional compliance alternative would achieve fewer emission reductions. EPA, *Regulatory Impact Analysis for the Proposed Carbon Pollution Guidelines for Existing Power Plants and Emission Standards for Modified and Reconstructed Power Plants*, June 2014, at http://www2.epa.gov/sites/ production/files/2014-06/documents/20140602ria-clean-power-plan.pdf.

[53] Using the full range of benefits reported in the Regulatory Impact Analysis using several discount rates.

[54] Interagency Working Group on Social Cost of Carbon, United States Government. Technical Support Document: - Technical Update of the Social Cost of Carbon for Regulatory Impact Analysis - Under Executive Order 12866. Washington, DC: Office of Management and Budget, November 2013. http://www.whitehouse.gov/sites/default/files/ omb/assets/inforeg /technical-update-social-cost-of-carbon-for-regulator-impact-analysis.pdf.

[55] Ibid., Section 1.

[56] 5 U.S.C. §§801-808.

[57] 5 U.S.C. §804(3).

[58] *Id.*; *see* 5 U.S.C. §551(4).

[59] *See* 5 U.S.C. §553(b).

[60] *See* 5 U.S.C. §553(c).

[61] GAO, "Congressional Review Act (CRA) FAQs," *available at* http://www.gao.gov/legal/congressact/cra_faq.html#6 ("[Question:] Should agencies submit proposed rules to GAO? [Answer:] No. Agencies should only submit major, nonmajor, and interim final rules to GAO.").

[62] Letter from the Honorable Mitch McConnell to the Honorable Gene L. Dodaro, Comptroller General, Government Accountability Office, January 16, 2014 [hereinafter McConnell GAO Letter].

[63] 79 *Federal Register* 1430, January 8, 2014.

[64] McConnell GAO Letter, *supra* note 62, at 1; *see* 42 U.S.C. §7411(a)(2).

[65] Letter from Susan A. Poling, General Counsel, Government Accountability Office, to the Honorable Harry Reid, Mitch McConnell, Barbara Boxer, and Thomas Carper, May 29, 2014 (regarding GAO's Role and Responsibility Under the Congressional Review Act) at 1 [hereinafter GAO May 2014 CRA Letter]. Specifically, GAO "agreed to answer three questions: (1) what is GAO's role under CRA and what type of agency action triggers that role; (2) what role does GAO play under CRA with regard to a proposed rule; and (3) do prior GAO opinions under CRA examining final agency actions outside of the rulemaking process provide precedent in answering these questions." *Id.*

[66] *Id.* at 5.

[67] *Id.* at 8.
[68] *Id.*
[69] *Id.* at 6.
[70] *See* U.S. CONST., art. I, §5, cl. 2.
[71] GAO May 2014 CRA Letter, *supra* note 65, at 9.

In: EPA's Proposed Carbon Dioxide Rule ...   ISBN: 978-1-63463-178-5
Editor: Carmella Ramos   © 2014 Nova Science Publishers, Inc.

Chapter 4

EPA REGULATION OF GREENHOUSE GASES: CONGRESSIONAL RESPONSES AND OPTIONS[*]

James E. McCarthy

SUMMARY

As a direct result of the Environmental Protection Agency's promulgation of an "endangerment finding" for greenhouse gas (GHG) emissions in December 2009, and its subsequent promulgation of GHG emission standards for new motor vehicles in 2010, the agency has proceeded to control GHG emissions from new and modified *stationary* sources as well. Stationary sources, including power plants, refineries, manufacturing facilities, and others account for about 70% of U.S. emissions of greenhouse gases. If the United States is to reduce its total GHG emissions, as President Obama has committed to do, it will be necessary to reduce emissions from these sources.

EPA's 2010 regulations limiting GHG emissions from new cars and light trucks triggered two Clean Air Act (CAA) provisions affecting stationary sources of air pollution. First, since January 2, 2011, new or modified major stationary sources must undergo New Source Review (NSR) with respect to their GHGs in addition to any other pollutants subject to regulation under the CAA that are emitted by the source. This review requires affected sources to install Best Available Control

---

[*] This is an edited, reformatted and augmented version of a Congressional Research Service publication R41212, prepared for Members and Committees of Congress, dated February 20, 2014.

Technology (BACT) to address their GHG emissions. Second, major sources of GHGs (existing and new) must now obtain permits under Title V of the CAA (or have existing permits modified to include their GHG requirements).

EPA shares congressional concerns about the potential scope of these provisions, primarily because a literal reading of the act would have required as many as 6 million stationary sources to obtain permits. To avoid this result, on May 13, 2010, the agency finalized a "Tailoring Rule" that focuses its resources on the largest emitters while deciding over a six-year period what to do about smaller sources.

Beyond these permitting requirements, EPA has begun the process of establishing emission standards for large stationary sources of GHGs under the act. Thus far, the agency has focused on electric generating units (EGUs), which account for about one-third of total U.S. GHG emissions. The agency proposed performance (emission) standards for new EGUs on January 8, 2014. Guidelines for existing EGUs are to be proposed by June 1.

Many in Congress have suggested that EPA should delay taking action on any stationary sources or should be prevented from doing so. There were at least 10 bills introduced in the 112th Congress that would have delayed or prevented EPA actions on greenhouse gas emissions, and legislation continues to be considered in the 113th. Among the bills introduced, recent attention has focused on H.R. 3826 and S.J.Res. 30. The former, which was ordered reported by the Energy and Commerce Committee, January 28, 2014, would prohibit EPA from promulgating or implementing GHG emission standards for fossil-fueled EGUs until certain stringent requirements were met, and would require that Congress enact new legislation setting an effective date before such standards could be implemented. The latter, a resolution of disapproval under the Congressional Review Act, would render EPA's proposed standards of no force or effect.

This report discusses elements of the GHG controversy, providing background on stationary sources of GHG pollution and identifying options Congress has at its disposal to address GHG issues, including (1) resolutions of disapproval under the Congressional Review Act; (2) freestanding legislation; (3) the use of appropriations bills as a vehicle to influence EPA activity; and (4) amendments to the Clean Air Act, including legislation to establish a new GHG control regime.

INTRODUCTION

On April 1, 2010, then-Administrator of the Environmental Protection Agency (EPA) Lisa Jackson signed final regulations that require auto manufacturers to limit emissions of greenhouse gases (GHGs) from new cars and light trucks.[1] These regulations have triggered two Clean Air Act provisions affecting *stationary* sources of air pollution such as electric power plants. First, effective January 2, 2011, new or modified major stationary sources have to undergo Prevention of Significant Deterioration/New Source Review (PSD-NSR) with respect to their GHG emissions in addition to any other pollutants subject to regulation under the Clean Air Act that they emit. This review requires affected sources to install Best Available Control Technology (BACT) to address their GHG emissions. Second, existing sources (in addition to new ones) have to obtain permits under Title V of the Clean Air Act (or have existing permits modified to include their GHG requirements). EPA has also proposed New Source Performance Standards under the Clean Air Act that would set national emission standards for new electric generating units (EGUs). EGUs account for about one-third of the nation's total GHG emissions.

EPA's potential regulation of GHG emissions (particularly from stationary sources) has led some in Congress to suggest that the agency delay taking action or be stopped from proceeding. In each Congress since the 111th, bills have been introduced to rescind or limit EPA's greenhouse gas authority.

EPA has attempted to respond to congressional concerns by clarifying the direction and schedule of its actions. However, the agency has been limited to the degree it can delineate specifics as many of the regulatory components, such as New Source Performance Standards (NSPS) for stationary sources, are in the early stages of the rulemaking process. EPA has provided three clear responses so far to the congressional concerns outlined above:

- The first came on March 29, 2010, when the Administrator reinterpreted a 2008 memorandum concerning the effective date of the stationary source permit requirements.[2] Facing a possibility of having to begin the permitting process on April 1, 2010 (the date the first GHG standard for automobiles was finalized), the March 29 decision delayed for nine months (to January 2, 2011) the date on which EPA would consider stationary source GHGs to be subject to regulation, and thus, subject to the permitting requirements of PSD-NSR and Title V.[3]

- On May 13, 2010, the Administrator signed the GHG "Tailoring" Rule, which provided for a phasing in of Title V and PSD-NSR permitting requirements, as discussed in detail below.

- On November 10, 2010, the EPA released a package of guidance and
  technical information to assist local and state permitting authorities in
  implementing PSD and Title V permitting for greenhouse gas
  emissions.[4]

The EPA Administrator and the President have repeatedly expressed their
preference for Congress to take the lead in designing a GHG regulatory
system. However, EPA simultaneously stated that, in the absence of
congressional action, it must proceed to regulate GHG emissions: a 2007
Supreme Court decision (*Massachusetts v. EPA*[5]) compelled EPA to address
whether GHGs are air pollutants that endanger public health and welfare, and
if so to embark on a regulatory course that is prescribed by statute. Having
made an affirmative decision to the endangerment question, EPA is now
proceeding with regulations.

Thus, EPA and a number of Members of Congress have been on a collision
course. EPA is proceeding to regulate emissions of GHGs under the Clean Air
Act, as it maintains it must, while trying to focus those efforts on the largest
emitters within a feasible timeframe. Opponents of this effort in Congress
continue to explore approaches to alter the agency's course.

The President, in his second inaugural address, promised to "respond to
the threat of climate change." On June 25, 2013, he directed EPA to propose[6]
New Source Performance Standards for greenhouse gas emissions from new
fossil-fueled power plants by September 20, 2013,[7] and to propose guidelines
for existing power plants by June 1, 2014. Thus, EPA is moving forward with
limits on greenhouse gas emissions from both new and existing power plants,
leaving Congress, once again, to consider how best to respond.

This report discusses elements of this controversy, providing background
on stationary sources of greenhouse gas pollution and identifying options
Congress has if it chooses to address the issue. The report discusses four sets
of options: (1) resolutions of disapproval under the Congressional Review Act;
(2) freestanding legislation directing, delaying, or prohibiting EPA action; (3)
the use of appropriations bills as a vehicle to influence EPA activity; and (4)
amendments to the Clean Air Act, including legislation to establish a new
GHG control regime. The report considers each of these in turn, but first
provides additional detail regarding the sources of GHG emissions, the
requirements of the Clean Air Act, and the significance of regulating
emissions from stationary sources.

REGULATION OF STATIONARY SOURCE GHGS

When EPA finalized its first regulation of greenhouse gas emissions from new mobile sources, legal and policy drivers were activated that have led to regulation of stationary sources as well. Stationary sources are the major sources of the country's GHG emissions. Overall, 69% of U.S. emissions of greenhouse gases come from stationary sources (the remainder come largely from mobile sources, primarily cars and trucks). Relatively large sources of fossil-fuel combustion and other industrial processes are responsible for more than half the country's total emissions (see *Table 1*). If EPA (or Congress) is to embark on a serious effort to reduce greenhouse gas emissions, stationary sources, and in particular large stationary sources, will have to be included.

Table 1. Selected U.S. Stationary Sources of Greenhouse Gases
(million metric tons of CO_2-equivalent)

Source	2011 Emissions	% of Total GHGs
Electricity Generation (CO_2, CH_4, N_2O)		
Coal-fired	1735.1	25.9%
Natural gas-fired	414.8	6.2%
Fuel oil-fired	26.6	0.4%
Industrial fossil-fuel combustion (CO_2, CH_4, N_2O) Mostly petroleum refineries, chemicals, primary metals, paper, food, and nonmetallic mineral products		
Coal-fired	90.7	1.4%
Natural gas-fired	416.8	6.2%
Fuel oil-fired	267.2	4.0%
Industrial Processes		
Iron and steel production (CO_2, CH_4)	64.9	1.0%
Cement production (CO2)	31.6	0.5%
Nitric acid production (N2O)	15.5	0.2%
Substitution for ozone-depleting substances (HFCs)	121.7	1.8%
Other		
Natural gas systems (CO2, CH_4)	177.0	2.6%
Landfills (CH_4)	103.0	1.5%
TOTAL	3464.9	51.7%

Source: EPA, Inventory of U.S. Greenhouse Gas Emissions and Sinks: 1990-2011, April 12, 2013.

The substantial amount of greenhouse gas emissions emanating from stationary source categories is even more important from a policy standpoint: reductions in greenhouse gas emissions from these sources are likely to be more timely and cost-effective than attempts to reduce emissions from the transport sector.

Two factors have driven the concerns about EPA's decisions on mobile sources spilling over to decisions on stationary sources: (1) the non-discretionary triggers within the CAA, discussed above, that impose permitting requirements on stationary sources because of the mobile source action; and (2) legal and policy linkages between mobile and stationary sources with respect to greenhouse gases that are likely to force EPA to issue additional endangerment findings and accompanying regulations on stationary sources. In particular, three potential impacts on stationary sources have raised the most concern:

- mandatory permitting requirements under the Prevention of Significant Deterioration / New Source Review (PSD-NSR) program (Sections 165-169);
- mandatory permitting requirements under Title V, the permit title of the Clean Air Act; and
- further endangerment findings that would require greenhouse gas reductions under different parts of the act,[8] particularly Section 111, New Source Performance Standards.

Prevention of Significant Deterioration / New Source Review (PSD-NSR)

Under Sections 165-169 of the Clean Air Act, any new or modified facility emitting (or potentially emitting) over 100 or 250 tons of any regulated pollutant[9] must undergo preconstruction review and permitting, including the installation of Best Available Control Technology (BACT) to limit emissions. State permitting agencies determine BACT on a case-by-case basis, taking into account energy, environmental, and economic impacts. BACT cannot be less stringent than the federal New Source Performance Standard, if there is one, but it can be more so.[10] EPA issues guidelines to states to assist them in making BACT determinations.[11]

PSD-NSR is required for any pollutant "subject to regulation" under the Clean Air Act. EPA maintains, based on an agency interpretation dating back to 1978,[12] that this requirement was triggered for GHGs when the agency's GHG regulations for cars and light trucks took effect January 2, 2011. The agency's interpretation has been challenged, unsuccessfully so far: the D.C. Circuit Court of Appeals sided with EPA unanimously in *Coalition for Responsible Regulation, Inc. v. EPA*[13]; but the Supreme Court has agreed to consider an appeal (*Utility Air Regulatory Group v. EPA*), with oral argument scheduled for February 24, 2014.[14]

Two aspects of invoking the New Source Review provision led EPA to issue regulations that modified its reach. First, as noted above, PSD-NSR has specified thresholds for triggering its provisions: a "major emitting facility" is defined as emitting or having the potential to emit either 100 tons or 250 tons annually of a regulated pollutant (Sec. 169(1)).[15] With respect to greenhouse gases, this is a very low threshold. EPA concludes that at 100 tons per year, even large residential and commercial structures could be required to obtain permits. By comparison, the Waxman-Markey bill (H.R. 2454) of the 111th Congress generally used 25,000 metric tons as a regulatory threshold.

The second administrative issue for PSD-NSR is the requirement that BACT be determined on a case-by-case basis. Combined with a 100-ton or 250-ton threshold, this would have meant a massive increase in state determinations of BACT: the resulting increased permit activity would be at least two orders of magnitude, according to EPA.

EPA has addressed this threshold problem in the Greenhouse Gas Tailoring Rule, signed by the Administrator May 13, 2010.[16] The rule phased in the PSD-NSR requirements:

- in Step 1, from January 2, 2011, to June 30, 2011, there were no new permitting actions due solely to GHG emissions. Only sources undertaking permitting actions anyway for other pollutants needed to address GHGs, with a threshold of 75,000 tons per year (tpy) of CO_2-equivalent (CO_2-e) for applicability;
- in Step 2, beginning July 1, 2011, new sources that are not subject to major source permit requirements for any other air pollutant require PSD-NSR and Title V permits if they have the potential to emit 100,000 tpy or more of CO_2-e. Modifications of sources not otherwise subject to permit requirements have a permit threshold of 75,000 tpy;
- in Step 3, which would have required a new rulemaking from EPA, the agency said it would consider lowering the permit threshold, but not below 50,000 tpy of CO_2-e, beginning July 1, 2013 (the agency

announced on March 8, 2012, however, that it would not lower the permit threshold[17]);

- in Step 4, the agency said it will complete a study by 2015 projecting the administrative burden of requiring permits from smaller sources, considering available streamlining measures, and will solicit comment on permanent exclusion of certain sources from PSD, Title V, or both requirements in a rulemaking to be completed by April 30, 2016.

EPA estimated that under Steps 1 and 2, 1,600 new or modified sources annually would be required to obtain NSR permits for their GHG emissions. Without the Tailoring Rule, the estimate was that 82,000 facilities would have required permits.[18] The actual number of permits has been substantially below the agency's estimate, however: as of January 2014, EPA and the states had issued only 143 GHG permits to stationary sources since the requirement was implemented in January 2011.[19]

Title V Permits

When invoked by EPA's mobile source action, Title V requires all new and existing facilities that have the potential to emit a GHG pollutant in amounts of 100 tons per year or more to obtain permits. This size threshold is even more stringent than the above NSR requirement. If not modified, it would have resulted in substantial numbers of smaller sources having to obtain a state permit for the first time (most larger sources already have permits because they emit other pollutants regulated under the act).

In the preamble to its Tailoring Rule, EPA estimated that more than 6 million sources would potentially be subject to Title V if the threshold remained at 100 tons per year of emissions.[20] Thus, like PSD-NSR, a major complication that Title V introduces is the potential for very small sources of greenhouse gases to need permits in order to operate (or continue operating). Furthermore, Title V requires that covered entities pay fees established by the permitting authority, and that the total fees be sufficient to cover the costs of running the permit program.

It should be noted that Title V permits are designed to help states and the EPA in enforcing a source's various Clean Air Act-related requirements; they do not impose any requirements themselves. They simply put all the affected facility's Clean Air Act requirements in one place to make enforcement more efficient. Thus, for large facilities that already have Title V permits because of their emission of other regulated pollutants, the addition of GHGs to that permit does not represent a significant additional administrative burden. It was the potential for millions of sources not currently required to have a Title V permit that would have to obtain one under GHG regulations that represented the additional burden identified here, and was the impetus for EPA's Tailoring Rule described above. As a result of the Tailoring Rule, EPA estimated that 15,500 sources annually would need to obtain Title V permits.

Potential GHG Emission Standards under Section 111

Because stationary sources are the largest source of greenhouse gas emissions, EPA is likely to be compelled to issue further endangerment findings under separate parts of the act, resulting in regulation of greenhouse gases from various categories of stationary sources.[21] There are numerous paths such regulation might take: in the immediate future, EPA is focusing on Section 111, New Source Performance Standards (NSPS).

New Source Performance Standards are emission limitations imposed on designated categories of major new (or substantially modified) stationary sources of air pollution. A new source is subject to NSPS regardless of its location or ambient air conditions. Section 111 provides authority for EPA to impose performance standards directly in the case of new (or modified) stationary sources (Section 111(b)), and through the states in the case of existing sources (Section 111(d)). The authority to impose performance standards on new and modified sources refers to any category of sources that the Administrator judges "causes, or contributes significantly to, air pollution which may reasonably be anticipated to endanger public health or welfare" (Sec. 111(b)(1)(A))— language similar to the endangerment and cause-or-contribute findings EPA promulgated for motor vehicles on December 15, 2009.

In establishing these standards, Section 111 gives EPA considerable flexibility with respect to the source categories regulated, the size of the sources regulated, the particular gases regulated, along with the timing and phasing-in of regulations (Sec. 111(b)(2)). This flexibility extends to the stringency of the regulations with respect to costs, and secondary effects, such as non-air-quality, health and environmental impacts, along with energy requirements. This flexibility is encompassed within the Administrator's authority to determine what control systems she determines have been "adequately demonstrated." (For discussion of what is meant by the term "adequately demonstrated," see CRS Report R43127, *EPA Standards for Greenhouse Gas Emissions from Power Plants: Many Questions, Some Answers.*) Standards of performance developed by the states for existing sources under Section 111(d) can be similarly flexible.

EPA proposed NSPS for fossil-fueled electric generating units (EGUs) on April 13, 2012.[22] After receiving 2.5 million public comments, the most on any proposed rule in EPA's 40-year history— and in response to a Presidential directive[23]—the agency withdrew the 2012 proposal and proposed a somewhat modified version of the rule on January 8, 2014. The Clean Air Act requires the promulgation of a final NSPS within one year of proposal—thus, by January 8, 2015. In addition, the President has directed the agency to propose guidelines for *existing* EGUs under Section 111(d) by June 1, 2014, with final action one year later.

The proposed NSPS would set standards for GHG emissions from both coal-fired and naturalgas-fired EGUs. Gas-fired plants would be able to meet the proposed standard without add-on emission controls, but coal-fired plants (which generate carbon dioxide (CO_2) at a rate at least double that of new combined cycle natural gas plants) would need to reduce CO_2 emissions by roughly 40% as compared to the best performing new coal-fired power plants currently in operation in order to meet the proposed standard. Achieving this would require the installation of partial carbon capture and storage systems at new coal-fired plants, an expensive technology not yet demonstrated on a large coal-fired EGU.

EPA states that this technology will soon be demonstrated by plants currently under construction, and that the rule will provide the certainty needed to stimulate the technology's further development. Opponents view EPA's rule as effectively prohibiting the construction of new coal-fired power plants. As a result, there is renewed interest in Congress in blocking EPA's regulatory actions.

CONGRESSIONAL OPTIONS

As noted earlier, if Congress would like to see a different approach to GHG controls than those on which EPA has embarked, including stopping the agency in its tracks, at least four sets of options are available to change the agency's course: the Congressional Review Act; freestanding legislation; appropriations riders; and amendments to the Clean Air Act. Among the most widely discussed options has been the Congressional Review Act.

Congressional Review Act[24]

The Congressional Review Act (CRA, 5 U.S.C. §§801-808), enacted in 1996, establishes special congressional procedures for disapproving a broad range of regulatory rules issued by federal agencies.[25] Before any rule covered by the act can take effect, the federal agency that promulgates the rule must submit it to both houses of Congress and the Government Accountability Office (GAO). If Congress passes a joint resolution disapproving the rule under procedures provided by the act, and the resolution becomes law,[26] the rule cannot take effect or continue in effect. Also, the agency may not reissue either that rule or any substantially similar one, except under authority of a subsequently enacted law.

The CRA has been much discussed as a tool for overturning EPA's regulatory actions on GHG emissions. In the 111th Congress, on December 15, 2009, four identical resolutions were introduced to disapprove the first of EPA's GHG rules, the endangerment finding[27]—one in the Senate (Senator Murkowski's S.J.Res. 26) and three in the House (Representative Jerry Moran's H.J.Res. 66, Representative Skelton's H.J.Res. 76, and Representative Barton's H.J.Res. 77). Of the four, one proceeded to a vote: on May 24, 2010, a unanimous-consent agreement was reached providing for a vote on S.J.Res. 26 under procedures similar to those provided by the CRA; on June 10, 2010, however, the Senate voted 47-53 not to take up the resolution.

The path to enactment of a CRA resolution is a steep one. In the nearly two decades since the CRA was enacted, only one resolution has ever been enacted.[28] The path is particularly steep if the President opposes the resolution's enactment, which would almost certainly be the case with a resolution disapproving an EPA rule for GHG emissions. The Obama Administration has made the reduction of GHG emissions one of its major goals; as a result, many have concluded that legislation restricting EPA's authority to act, if passed by Congress, would encounter a presidential veto. Overriding a veto requires a two-thirds majority in both the House and Senate.

The potential advantage of the Congressional Review Act lies primarily in the procedures under which a resolution of disapproval is to be considered in the Senate. Pursuant to the act, an expedited procedure for Senate consideration of a disapproval resolution may be used at any time within 60 days of Senate session after the rule in question has been published in the *Federal Register* and received by both houses of Congress. The expedited procedure provides that, if the committee to which a disapproval resolution has been referred has not reported it by 20 calendar days after the rule has been received by Congress and published in the *Federal Register*, the panel may be discharged if 30 Senators submit a petition for that purpose. The resolution is then placed on the Calendar.

Under the expedited procedure, once a disapproval resolution is on the Calendar in the Senate, a motion to proceed to consider it is in order. Several provisions of the expedited procedure protect against various potential obstacles to the Senate's ability to take up a disapproval resolution. The Senate has treated a motion to consider a disapproval resolution under the CRA as not debatable, so that this motion cannot be filibustered through extended debate. After the Senate takes up the disapproval resolution itself, the expedited procedure of the CRA protects the ability of the body to continue and complete that consideration. It limits debate to 10 hours and prohibits amendments.[29]

The Congressional Review Act sets no deadline for final congressional action on a disapproval resolution, so a resolution could theoretically be brought to the Senate floor even after the expiration of the deadline for the use of the CRA's expedited procedures. To obtain floor consideration, the bill's supporters would then have to follow the Senate's normal procedures.

Similarly, a resolution could reach the House floor through its ordinary procedures, that is, generally by being reported by the committee of jurisdiction (in the case of EPA rules, the Energy and Commerce Committee). If the committee of jurisdiction does not report a disapproval resolution submitted in the House, a resolution could still reach the floor pursuant to a special rule reported by the Committee on Rules (and adopted by the House), by a motion to suspend the rules and pass it (requiring a two-thirds vote), or by discharge of the committee (requiring a majority of the House [218 Members] to sign a petition).

The CRA establishes no expedited procedure for further congressional action on a disapproval resolution if the President vetoes it. In such a case, Congress would need to attempt an override of a veto using its normal procedures for considering vetoed bills.

In the 113th Congress, Senator McConnell along with 41 cosponsors introduced S.J.Res. 30, to disapprove of an EPA proposed rule regarding New Source Performance Standards for electric generating units published in the *Federal Register* on January 8, 2014.[30] Although historically the CRA is considered not to apply to proposed rules,[31] Senator McConnell argued in a letter to GAO that the CRA should apply to this particular proposed rule based upon his interpretation of the immediate legal effect of the rule.[32] The CRA does not directly address the distinction between proposed and final rules, referring only to "a rule" or "the rule" as defined in Title 5, Section 551 of the U.S. Code (the Administrative Procedure Act), with specific exceptions.[33] Section 551 also does not directly address the definition of a proposed rule or the difference between a proposed and final rule, simply stating that a rule is "the whole or part of an agency statement of general or particular applicability and future effect designed to implement, interpret, or prescribe law or policy.... " There is no case law examining the applicability of the CRA to proposed rules; in fact, Section 805 of the CRA prohibits judicial review of determinations, findings, actions, or omissions under the act. Rather, Section 802 specifies that the CRA is "an exercise of the rulemaking power of the Senate and House of Representatives, respectively, and as such it is deemed a part of the rules of each House," presumably leaving it to the Senate Parliamentarian to decide whether or not the CRA would apply to a resolution disapproving of a proposed rule.

In practice, the Parliamentarian tends to defer to analysis on the applicability of the CRA requested by Members of Congress and conducted by GAO, which is also required under Section 801 of the CRA to submit a report on each major rule to the committees of jurisdiction in the House and Senate. Senator McConnell has requested that the GAO "review and determine Congress's authority to take up a resolution under the Congressional Review Act" in regards to the proposed rule.[34] As of this writing, GAO had not responded to Senator McConnell's letter.[35]

If the Parliamentarian determines that the EPA proposed rule is a rule for the purposes of the CRA and a resolution of disapproval is properly brought under the CRA, Senator McConnell could take advantage of the CRA expedited procedures in the Senate. S.J.Res. 30 was referred to the Environment and Public Works Committee, which is unlikely to report it for floor consideration; but, assuming the resolution falls within the CRA, with 41 cosponsors, Senator McConnell would presumably be able to meet the CRA's threshold of 30 signatures on a discharge petition to bring the resolution to the floor.[36]

Freestanding/Targeted Legislation

To provide for a more nuanced response to the issue than permitted under the CRA, Members have introduced freestanding legislation or legislation that amends the Clean Air Act in a targeted way. At least 10 bills (and several amendments) were introduced in the 112th Congress that would have prohibited temporarily or permanently EPA's regulation of greenhouse gas emissions, and legislation continues to be considered in the 113th Congress. These bills face the same obstacle as a CRA resolution of disapproval, however (i.e., being subject to a presidential veto). Among those introduced, attention in the 113th Congress focuses on Representative Whitfield's H.R. 3826, the Electricity Security and Affordability Act, which was ordered reported by the Energy and Commerce Committee on January 28, 2014.

H.R. 3826

H.R. 3826 would prohibit EPA from promulgating or implementing GHG emission standards for fossil-fueled power plants until at least six power plants representative of the operating characteristics of electric generation units at different locations across the United States have demonstrated compliance with proposed emission limits for a continuous period of 12 months on a commercial basis. Projects demonstrating the feasibility of carbon capture and storage that received government financial assistance could not be used in setting such standards, and the standards would not take effect unless Congress enacted new legislation setting an effective date. Given the role of the U.S. Department of Energy in financing demonstrations of clean coal technology and the cost of developing new emissions control technologies not required by regulation, the bill would effectively prohibit EPA from promulgating New Source Performance Standards for GHG emissions from EGUs. The agency's current NSPS proposal would set a standard that no coal-fired EGU currently meets, and it relies on technology that is being implemented with financial assistance from the Department of Energy.

The bill is expected to reach the House floor, but its prospects in the Senate (assuming it passes the House) are uncertain. If it passed both the Senate and House, the bill would almost certainly be subject to a Presidential veto.

Earlier Bills

In the 112th Congress, attention focused on several bills that passed the House and/or were considered in the Senate. Senator Rockefeller's S. 231, entitled the EPA Stationary Source Regulations Suspension Act, and its companion, Representative Capito's H.R. 199, would have provided that during the two-year period beginning on the date of their enactment, EPA could not take any action under the Clean Air Act with respect to any stationary source permitting requirement or any requirement under the New Source Performance Standards section of the act relating to carbon dioxide or methane.[37] A stated reason for the two-year delay was to allow Congress to enact legislation specifically designed to address climate change. The Senate bill was offered as an amendment to S. 493 (S.Amdt. 215) on April 6, 2011, and was not agreed to, on a vote of 12-88.

In addition to the Rockefeller amendment, other amendments to S. 493 addressing EPA's greenhouse gas authority were also considered. One was Senator Baucus's S.Amdt. 236; the other was S.Amdt. 277, authored by Senator Stabenow and Senator Sherrod Brown. Senator Baucus's amendment would have set thresholds (similar to EPA's "Tailoring Rule") to exempt most sources of greenhouse gas emissions from having to obtain Clean Air Act permits for those emissions. It would also have excluded agricultural sources from PSD-NSR permitting requirements based on their GHG emissions. The Stabenow-Brown amendment would have suspended EPA greenhouse gas requirements for stationary sources, including permits and New Source Performance Standards, for a two-year period. It would have exempted GHG emissions from agricultural sources from regulation. And it would have extended the tax credit for Advanced Energy Projects, with an authorization of $5 billion. Both the Baucus and Stabenow-Brown amendments were not agreed to, April 6, 2011, on votes of 7-93.

Legislation that received broader support in the 112th Congress, H.R. 910/S. 482, introduced by Chairman Upton of the House Energy and Commerce Committee and Senator Inhofe, then-ranking Member of the Senate Environment and Public Works Committee, would have permanently removed EPA's authority to regulate greenhouse gases. The House version passed, 255-177, April 7, 2011. In the Senate, Senator McConnell introduced language identical to the bill as an amendment to S. 493 (S.Amdt. 183). The amendment was not agreed to, on a vote of 50-50, April 6, 2011. The Upton-Inhofe-McConnell bill would have repealed a dozen EPA greenhouse-gas-related regulations, including the Mandatory Greenhouse Gas Reporting rule, the Endangerment Finding, and the PSD and Title V permitting requirements. It would have redefined the term "air pollutant" to exclude greenhouse gases. And it stated that EPA may not "promulgate any regulation concerning, take action related to, or take into consideration the emission of a greenhouse gas to address climate change." The bill would have had no effect on federal research, development, and demonstration programs. The already promulgated light-duty motor vehicle GHG standards and the GHG emission standards for Medium- and Heavy-Duty Engines and Vehicles would have been allowed to stay in effect, but no future mobile source rules for GHG emissions would have been allowed. Also, EPA would have been prohibited from granting another California waiver for greenhouse gas controls from mobile sources.

Appropriations Bills

A third option that Congress has used to delay regulatory initiatives is to place an amendment, or "rider" on the agency's appropriation bill that prevents funds from being used for the targeted initiative. In comparison to a CRA resolution of disapproval or freestanding legislation, addressing the issue through an amendment to the EPA appropriation—an approach that has been discussed at some length beginning in 2009—may be considered easier. The overall appropriation bill to which it would be attached would presumably contain other elements that would make it more difficult to veto.

In the last several Congresses, however, it has become difficult to move appropriations bills. The result has generally been that government agencies, EPA included, have been funded through continuing resolutions or omnibus appropriation bills that have few riders.

The FY2011-FY2014 appropriation processes are illustrative. In its FY2011 budget submission,[38] EPA requested $43 million for "additional regulatory efforts aimed at taking action on climate change," $25 million "for state grants focused on developing technical capacity to address greenhouse gas emissions under the Clean Air Act," and $13.5 million "for implementing new emission standards that will reduce Greenhouse Gas (GHG) emissions from mobile sources" including "developing potential standards for large transportation sources such as locomotives and aircraft engines, and analyzing the potential need for standards under petitions relating to major stationary sources."[39] These were small sums relative to the total agency budget request of slightly more than $10 billion, but GHG regulations were among the most controversial questions at congressional hearings on the agency's budget submission. Thus, it was not surprising to see amendments to the EPA appropriation and report language limiting or delaying EPA's GHG regulatory actions.

FY2011 appropriations for EPA and the rest of the government were provided through early April, 2011, by a series of continuing resolutions, leaving the question of EPA appropriations and potential riders affecting the agency's GHG regulatory efforts for the 112th Congress to decide. In February, 2011, language prohibiting EPA funding for a GHG regulatory requirement on stationary sources was added to the Full-Year Continuing Appropriations Act,

2011 bill (H.R. 1) during floor debate on a 249-177 vote (H.Amdt. 101), and the House subsequently passed the bill. However, the Senate failed to pass the bill, 44-56, March 9, 2011. Ultimately, Congress approved the Department of Defense and Full Year Continuing Appropriations Act, 2011 (H.R. 1473, P.L. 112-10) to provide continuing appropriations in lieu of 12 separate appropriations bills, and did not include the rider prohibiting stationary source GHG regulatory activity.[40]

Similarly, language prohibiting FY2012 funding for EPA GHG regulatory actions was added to H.R. 2584, the Interior, Environment, and Related Agencies Appropriations Act, 2012, which was reported by the Appropriations Committee July 19, 2011. As reported, the bill would have prohibited EPA (during the one-year period following enactment) from proposing or promulgating New Source Performance Standards for GHG emissions from electric generating units and refineries; would have declared any statutory or regulatory GHG permit requirement to be of no legal effect; would have prohibited common law or civil tort actions related to greenhouse gases or climate change, including nuisance claims, from being brought or maintained; would have prohibited the preparation, proposal, promulgation, finalization, implementation, or enforcement of regulations governing GHG emissions from motor vehicles manufactured after model year 2016, or the granting of a waiver to California so that it might implement such standards; and would have prohibited EPA from requiring the issuance of permits for GHG emissions from livestock and prohibited requiring the reporting of GHG emissions from manure management systems. The bill came to the House floor under an open rule during the last week of July, 2011, and about 200 amendments were filed for consideration. Action on the bill was suspended July 28, with more than 150 amendments still pending. Ultimately, only the livestock and manure provisions—which had been in two previous years' appropriations bills— were contained in EPA's FY2012 appropriation. The final bill, P.L. 112-74, consolidated 9 of the 12 regular appropriations bills into a single bill.[41]

There were similar provisions in H.R. 6091, as reported, for FY2013,[42] but again, most of the riders fell by the wayside when Congress enacted the Consolidated and Further Continuing Appropriations Act, 2013 (P.L. 113-6).

For FY2014, GHG regulations were again a major subject of interest in hearings on EPA's appropriation request. The House Appropriations Committee did not even report a bill to provide FY2014 EPA appropriations, however, which again were provided through an omnibus bill (P.L. 113-76) with few riders.

Throughout this process, the only riders affecting EPA's GHG regulatory authority that have been enacted have dealt with the potential regulation of agricultural sources of GHGs. The FY2014 appropriation and every previous EPA appropriation since FY2010 have included such provisions: Section 420, in Title IV of Division G under the Consolidated Appropriations Act, 2014 (P.L. 113-76) provides that "none of the funds made available in this Act or any other Act may be used to promulgate or implement any regulation requiring the issuance of permits under Title V of the Clean Air Act ... for carbon dioxide, nitrous oxide, water vapor, or methane emissions resulting from biological processes associated with livestock production." Section 421 prohibits the use of funds to implement mandatory reporting of GHG emissions from manure management systems.

Comprehensive Amendments to the Clean Air Act

The most comprehensive approach that Congress might take to alter EPA's course would be to amend the Clean Air Act to modify EPA's current regulatory authority as it pertains to GHGs and to provide alternative authority to address the GHG emissions issue. In the 111th Congress, this was the option chosen by the House in passing H.R. 2454, the American Clean Energy and Security Act (the Waxman-Markey bill) and by the Senate Environment and Public Works Committee in its reporting of S. 1733, the Clean Energy Jobs and American Power Act (the Kerry-Boxer bill). The bills would have amended the Clean Air Act to establish an economy-wide cap-and-trade program for GHGs, established a separate cap-and-trade program for HFCs, preserved EPA's authority to regulate GHG emissions from mobile sources while setting deadlines for regulating specific mobile source categories, and required the setting of New Source Performance Standards for uncapped major sources of GHGs.

While giving EPA new authority, at the same time both bills contained provisions to limit EPA's authority to set GHG standards or regulate GHG emissions under Sections 108 (National Ambient Air Quality Standards), 112 (Hazardous Air Pollutants), 115 (International Air Pollution), 165 (PSD-NSR), and Title V (Permits) because of the climate effects of these pollutants.[43] The bills would not have prevented EPA from acting under these authorities if one or more of these gases proved to have effects other than climate effects that endanger public health or welfare.

With respect to exemption from the permitting requirements of the PSD program and Title V, the bills differed in the extent of their exemptions. The H.R. 2454 provision would have prevented new or modified stationary sources from coming under the PSD-NSR program solely because they emit GHGs. In contrast, the Senate bill's provision would have simply raised the threshold for regulation under PSD from the current 100 or 250 short tons to 25,000 metric tons with respect to any GHG, or combination of GHGs. Likewise, with respect to Title V permitting, the H.R. 2454 provision would have prevented any source (large or small) from having to obtain a state permit under Title V solely because they emit GHGs. In contrast, the exemption under the Senate bill was restricted to sources that emit under 25,000 metric tons of any GHG or combination of GHGs.[44]

Amending the Clean Air Act to revoke some existing regulatory authority as it pertains to GHGs while establishing new authority designed specifically to address their emissions is the approach that was advocated by the Administration and, indeed, by many participants in the climate debate regardless of their position on EPA's regulatory initiatives. However, the specifics of a bill acceptable to a majority would be difficult to craft.

CONCLUSION

In some respects, EPA's greenhouse gas decisions are similar to actions it has taken previously for other pollutants. Beginning in 1970, and reaffirmed by amendments in 1977 and 1990, Congress gave the agency broad authority to identify pollutants and to proceed with regulation. Congress did not itself identify the pollutants to be covered by National Ambient Air Quality Standards (NAAQS), for example; rather, it told the agency to identify pollutants that are emitted by numerous and diverse sources, and the presence of which in ambient air endangers public health and welfare. EPA has used this authority to regulate six pollutants or groups of pollutants, the so-called "criteria pollutants."[45] EPA also has authority under other sections of the act—notably Sections 111 (New Source Performance Standards), 112 (Hazardous Air Pollutants), and 202 (Motor Vehicle Emission Standards)—to identify pollutants on its own initiative and promulgate emission standards for them.

Actions with regard to GHGs follow these precedents and can use the same statutory authorities. The differences are of scale and of degree. Greenhouse gases are global pollutants to a greater extent than most of the pollutants previously regulated under the act;[46] reductions in U.S. emissions without simultaneous reductions by other countries may somewhat diminish but will not solve the problems the emissions cause.[47] Also, GHGs are such pervasive pollutants, and arise from so many sources, that reducing the emissions may have broader effects on the economy than most previous EPA regulations.

EPA's focus on Section 111 as the principal vehicle for controlling GHGs from stationary sources may reflect concerns both about potential economic effects and about implementation difficulties with respect to controlling such pervasive pollutants. Indeed, in a 2008 *Federal Register* notice, EPA made an argument that authority for a market-based control program may exist under Section 111.[48] Even if that argument fails to pass legal scrutiny, the section does provide EPA with substantial authority to address economic and implementation issues in tailoring its GHG response to the various realities surrounding stationary source controls.

Nevertheless, as noted, the Administration's position has been that a new market-based program authorized by new legislation is the preferred option for controlling GHGs. New legislation has also been the preferred option of many in Congress, regardless of whether they agree or disagree with EPA's regulatory initiatives. Until the issue is resolved through legislative negotiations or through legal or regulatory venues, EPA will likely proceed under existing authorities of the Clean Air Act and the complex interplay of legal, regulatory, and legislative events will continue.

End Notes

[1] The regulations, which took effect with the 2012 model year, appeared in the Federal Register on May 7, 2010, at 75 Federal Register 25324. Related information is available on EPA's website at http://www.epa.gov/otaq/climate/ regulations.htm.

[2] The reinterpretation memo appeared in the Federal Register, April 2, 2010, at 75 Federal Register 17004.

[3] The term "subject to regulation" is the key Clean Air Act term that determines when affected sources would be subject to the permitting requirements of NSR and Title V. By interpreting the term to refer to January 2, 2011, rather than the date of the final regulations implementing the mobile source endangerment finding (April 1, 2010), EPA effectively delayed the impact of that rulemaking on stationary sources for nine months. For a further discussion of the term, "subject to regulation," see CRS Report R40984, Legal Consequences of EPA's Endangerment Finding for New Motor Vehicle Greenhouse Gas Emissions.

[4] U.S. EPA, Office of Air and Radiation, "PSD and Title V Permitting Guidance for Greenhouse Gases," November 2010 (subsequently revised, March 2011), at http://www.epa.gov/nsr/ghgdocs/ghgpermittingguidance.pdf.

[5] 549 U.S. 497 (2007). For more information, see CRS Report R41505, EPA's BACT Guidance for Greenhouse Gases from Stationary Sources.

[6] Actually, he directed EPA to re-propose the standards. The NSPS were first proposed on April 13, 2012. EPA received more public comments on the rule than any rule in its 40-year history, and had not completed action on the original proposal.

[7] The re-proposed standards were signed September 20, and were published in the Federal Register, January 8, 2014, at 79 Federal Register 1430.

[8] For a further discussion of the act's various endangerment finding provisions, see CRS Report R40984, Legal Consequences of EPA's Endangerment Finding for New Motor Vehicle Greenhouse Gas Emissions.

[9] Except those pollutants regulated under Sections 112 (hazardous air pollutants) and 211(o) (renewable fuels).

[10] The PSD program (Part C of Title I of the CAA) focuses on ambient concentrations of sulfur dioxide (SO2), nitrogen oxides (NOx), and particulate matter (PM) in "clean" air areas of the country (i.e., areas where air quality is better than the air quality standards (NAAQS)). The program allows some increase in clean areas' pollution concentrations depending on their classification. In general, historic or recreation areas (e.g., national parks) are classified Class I with very little degradation allowed, while most other areas are classified Class II with moderate degradation allowed. States are allowed to reclassify Class II areas to Class III areas, which would be permitted to degrade up to the NAAQS, but none have ever been reclassified to Class III. There are no PSD emission limitations for GHGs, nor is there a NAAQS for GHGs. This presumably gives EPA and the states increased latitude in determining how much additional GHG pollution can be allowed by a new or modified source.

[11] See CRS Report R41505, EPA's BACT Guidance for Greenhouse Gases from Stationary Sources.

[12] 43 Federal Register 26382, June 19, 1978.

[13] 684 F.3d 102 (D.C.Cir. 2012).

[14] Docket No. 12-1146.

[15] Section 169(1) lists 28 categories of sources for which the threshold is to be 100 tons of emissions per year. For all other sources, the threshold is 250 tons. It should be noted that a different threshold applies in the case of major modifications, which are defined by regulation, not statute. For sulfur dioxide and nitrogen oxides, the threshold for a major modification is an increase in emissions of 40 tons per year. Facilities exceeding that threshold are subject to NSR. Given that EPA has identified by regulation the de minimis emission increases for triggering NSR review for modifications, it is possible EPA could set a substantially higher level for at least carbon dioxide emissions, and perhaps other greenhouse gases, if it determined such thresholds were appropriate. In the final Tailoring Rule, the agency set a threshold of 75,000 tons per year of CO2-equivalent for applying NSR to modifications.

[16] The rule appeared in the June 3, 2010, Federal Register. See U.S. EPA, "Prevention of Significant Deterioration and Title V Greenhouse Gas Tailoring Rule," 75 Federal Register 31514. A six-page EPA Fact Sheet summarizing the rule is available at http://www.epa. gov/nsr/documents/20100413fs.pdf.

[17] 77 Federal Register 14226.

[18] U.S. EPA, Office of Air Quality Planning and Standards, "Summary of Clean Air Act Permitting Burdens With and Without the Tailoring Rule," p. 6, at http://www.epa.gov/ nsr/documents/20100413piecharts.pdf.

[19] The number of permits was provided in a personal communication from EPA's Office of Air Quality Planning and Standards.

[20] 75 Federal Register 31547, Table VI-1, p. 31547. All but 3% of these sources would be commercial establishments and large residences, according to EPA.

[21] For a discussion of the similarities and differences in the various endangerment findings contained in the Clean Air Act, see CRS Report R40984, Legal Consequences of EPA's Endangerment Finding for New Motor Vehicle Greenhouse Gas Emissions.

[22] U.S. EPA, Standards of Performance for Greenhouse Gas Emissions for New Stationary Sources: Electric Utility Generating Units, Proposed Rule, 77 Federal Register 22392, April 13, 2012.

[23] Office of the Press Secretary, The White House, "Power Sector Carbon Pollution Standards," Memorandum for the Administrator of the Environmental Protection Agency, June 25, 2013, at http://www.whitehouse.gov/the-press-office/2013/06/25/presidential-memorandum -power-sector-carbon-pollution-standards.

[24] This section of this report, discussing the effect of the Congressional Review Act, the procedures under which a disapproval resolution is taken up in the Senate, floor consideration in the Senate, and final congressional action, is adapted from CRS Report RL31160, Disapproval of Regulations by Congress: Procedure Under the Congressional Review Act, by Richard S. Beth. Additional input to this section was provided by Alissa Dolan, Legislative Attorney, American Law Division of CRS.

[25] The CRA applies to a "rule," as defined in 5 U.S.C. §804(3).

[26] For the resolution to become law, the President must sign it or allow it to become law without his signature, or the Congress must override a presidential veto.

[27] 74 Federal Register 66496. While generally referred to as the "endangerment finding" (singular), the Federal Register notice consists of two separate findings: a Finding that Emissions of Greenhouse Gases Endanger Public Health and Welfare, and a Finding That Greenhouse Gases from Motor Vehicles Cause or Contribute to the Endangerment of Public Health and Welfare.

[28] See P.L. 107-5 (2001) (disapproving of an Occupational Safety and Health Administration Rule regarding ergonomics published at 65 Federal Register 68261).

[29] These provisions help to ensure that the Senate disapproval resolution will remain identical, at least in substantive effect, to the House joint resolution disapproving the same rule, so that no filibuster is possible on the resolution itself. In addition, once the motion to proceed is adopted, the resolution becomes "the unfinished business of the Senate until disposed of," and a non-debatable motion may be offered to limit the time for debate further. Finally, the act provides that at the conclusion of debate, the Senate automatically proceeds to vote on the resolution.

[30] U.S. EPA, Standards of Performance for Greenhouse Gas Emissions From New Stationary Sources: Electric Utility Generating Units, Proposed Rule, 79 Federal Register 1430, January 8, 2014.

[31] See, for example, GAO's Congressional Review Act FAQs, available at http://www.gao. gov/legal/congressact/ cra_faq.html.

[32] Letter of Senator Mitch McConnell to Hon. Gene L. Dodaro, Comptroller General of the United States, January 16, 2014, available at http://www.washingtonpost.com/r/2010-2019/WashingtonPost/2014/01/16/National-Politics/ Graphics/MM%20letter%20to%20GAO-CRA.pdf. In the letter, Senator McConnell stated that he was "not asking the GAO to address the question of whether all proposed rules are eligible for CRA review.... Ordinarily, the publication of a proposed rule by EPA (or any

other agency) does not have any immediate legal impact.... However, the Proposed GHG Rule was issued under Section 111(b) of the CAA, which contains a highly unusual 'applicability' provision. Any power plant whose construction is commenced 'after the publication of regulations (or, if earlier, proposed regulations) prescribing a standard of performance ... which will be applicable to such source' is considered to be a 'new source' subject to that standard," and, therefore, the proposed rule should be considered a rule under the CRA.

[33] The CRA definition of a rule does not include (1) any rule of particular applicability, including a rule that approves or prescribes for the future rates, wages, prices, services, or allowances therefor, corporate or financial structures, reorganizations, mergers, or acquisitions thereof, or accounting practices or disclosures bearing on any of the foregoing; (2) any rule relating to agency management or personnel; or (3) any rule of agency organization, procedure, or practice that does not substantially affect the rights or obligations of non-agency parties. 5 U.S.C. §804(3).

[34] Letter of Senator Mitch McConnell to Hon. Gene L. Dodaro, Comptroller General of the United States, January 16, 2014, available at http://www.washingtonpost.com/r/2010-2019/WashingtonPost/2014/01/16/National-Politics/Graphics/MM%20letter%20to%20GAO-CRA.pdf.

[35] If the Parliamentarian were to determine that the EPA proposed rule is a "rule" for the purposes of the CRA based on such an opinion from GAO, based on past practice, it is likely that the Parliamentarian would use the date of GAO's opinion as the earliest possible date for the introduction of a CRA resolution of disapproval under Section 802(a). See Press Release, U.S. Senate Committee on Finance, "Senators Vow to Keep Fighting for Children's Health Care" (July 22, 2008) available at http://www.finance.senate.gov/newsroom/chairman/release/?id=363028c1-c4fe-4ca9-b180-746e3e9daf82 ("The Parliamentarian concluded that the 60-day clock started on the date of the April 17th GAO letter determining that the CHIP directive was a rule for the purposes of the CRA.").Therefore, it is possible that even if GAO and the Parliamentarian were to determine that the EPA proposed rule is subject to the CRA that S.J.Res. 30 would not be eligible for the expedited procedures available under the CRA because it would have been introduced before the period for introducing a resolution of disapproval under the statute. Senator McConnell would then have to introduce a new resolution within the 60 day period beginning on the date of the GAO opinion in order to take advantage of the CRA's expedited procedures.

[36] Given that Senator McConnell could use the CRA's discharge procedures to move the resolution out of Committee, it is possible that the Committee could choose to report the measure unfavorably.

[37] The phrase "relating to carbon dioxide or methane," presumably modified both the permitting and regulation-setting prohibitions.

[38] EPA's appropriations are part of the Interior, Environment, and Related Agencies appropriation.

[39] Testimony of Lisa P. Jackson, Administrator, U.S. Environmental Protection Agency, "Hearing on the President's Proposed EPA Budget for FY 2011," Senate Environment and Public Works Committee, February 23, 2010, pp. 2-3.

[40] For additional information, see CRS Report R41698, H.R. 1 Full-Year FY2011 Continuing Resolution: Overview of Environmental Protection Agency (EPA) Provisions, by Robert Esworthy.

[41] For additional information, see CRS Report R41979, Environmental Protection Agency (EPA) FY2012 Appropriations: Overview of Provisions in H.R. 2584 as Reported, by Robert Esworthy.

[42] For additional information, see Table C-1 in CRS Report R42520, Environmental Protection Agency (EPA) Appropriations for FY2013: Debate During the 112th Congress, coordinated by Robert Esworthy.

[43] The Clean Air Act exemption provisions under H.R. 2454 were in Part C, Sections 831-835; under S. 1733, the provisions were in Section 128(g).

[44] For further information, see CRS Report R40896, Climate Change: Comparison of the Cap-and-Trade Provisions in H.R. 2454 and S. 1733.

[45] The six are ozone, particulate matter, carbon monoxide, sulfur dioxide, nitrogen dioxide, and lead.

[46] An exception would be chlorofluorocarbons, regulated under Title VI of the act to protect the stratospheric ozone layer. This also was a global problem, but in this case an international agreement, the Montreal Protocol, preceded EPA action and the enactment of Clean Air Act authority.

[47] However, the Administration is working in parallel internationally to obtain commitments to global GHG reductions. Demonstrating timely and significant progress toward reduction of U.S. GHG emissions is considered essential by most experts for success internationally.

[48] U.S. Environmental Protection Agency, "Regulating Greenhouse Gas Emissions Under the Clean Air Act; Proposed Rule," 73 Federal Register 44514-44516, July 30, 2008. Whether EPA can set up a cap-and-trade program under the Clean Air Act has been the subject of considerable debate in the literature. See Lisa Heinzerling, Testimony Before the Subcommittee on Energy and Air Quality of the Committee on Energy and Commerce, Hearing (April 10, 2008); Robert R. Nordhaus, "New Wine into Old Bottles: The Feasibility of Greenhouse Gas Regulation Under the Clean Air Act," N.Y.U. Environmental Law Journal (2007), pp. 53-72; Inimai M. Chettiar and Jason A. Schwartz, The Road Ahead: EPA's Options and Obligations For Regulating Greenhouse Gases (April 2009); Alaine Ginocchio et al., The Boundaries of Executive Authority: Using Executive Orders to Implement Federal Climate Change Policy (February 2008); Nathan Richardson, "Playing Without Aces: Offsets and the Limits of Flexibility Under the Cean Air Act Climate Policy, 42 Envtl. L. 735, 738 (2012); and Gregory Wannier et al., "Prevailing Academic View on Compliance Flexibility Under §111 of the Clean Air Act," Discussion Paper 11-29 (Resources for the Future 2011).

In: EPA's Proposed Carbon Dioxide Rule ...   ISBN: 978-1-63463-178-5
Editor: Carmella Ramos   © 2014 Nova Science Publishers, Inc.

Chapter 5

BY THE NUMBERS: CUTTING CARBON POLLUTION FROM POWER PLANTS[*]

Environmental Protection Agency

On June 2, 2014, the U.S. Environmental Protection Agency, under President Obama's Climate Action Plan, proposed a commonsense plan to cut carbon pollution from power plants. The science shows that climate change is already posing risks to our health and our economy. The Clean Power Plan will maintain an affordable, reliable energy system, while cutting pollution and protecting our health and environment now and for future generations.

CLEANING UP POWER PLANTS

- Power plants are the *largest source* of carbon dioxide emissions in the United States, making up roughly *one-third* of all domestic greenhouse gas emissions.
- All told—the Plan puts our nation on track to cut carbon pollution from the power sector by *30 percent* by 2030—that's about *730 million metric tonnes* of carbon pollution.

---

[*] This is an edited, reformatted and augmented version of an EPA Fact Sheet for the proposed Clean Power Plan, issued June 2014.

- That's equal to the annual emissions from more than *150 million cars*, or almost *2/3s of the nation's passenger vehicles* – or the annual emissions from powering *65 million homes, over half the homes in America.*

BIG PUBLIC HEALTH AND CLIMATE BENEFITS

- The Clean Power Plan has public health and climate benefits worth an estimated *$55 billion to $93 billion* per year in 2030, far outweighing the costs of *$7.3 billion to $8.8 billion.*
- Reducing exposure to particle pollution and ozone in 2030 will avoid a projected
  o 2,700 to 6,600 premature deaths
  o 140,000 to 150,000 asthma attacks in children
  o 340 to 3,300 heart attacks
  o 2,700 to 2,800 hospital admissions
  o 470,000 to 490,000 missed school and work days
- From the soot and smog reductions alone, for every dollar invested through the Clean Power Plan—American families will see up to $7 in health benefits.
- The Clean Power Plan will reduce pollutants that contribute to the soot and smog that make people sick by over 25 percent in 2030.
  o 54,000 to 56,000 tons of PM2.5
  o 424,000 to 471,000 tons of sulfur dioxide
  o 407,000 to 428,000 tons of nitrogen dioxide

NUMBER OF POWER PLANTS COVERED BY THE CLEAN POWER PLAN

- In the U.S., there are 1,000 fossil fuel fired power plants with 3,000 units covered by this rule.
- Utility planners are already making plans to address an aging fleet. The average age of coal units is 42 years. The average age of oil units is 36 years. The average age of natural gas combined cycle units is 14 years.

STATE CLIMATE, ENERGY EFFICIENCY AND RENEWABLE ENERGY POLICY STATISTICS

- States, cities and businesses have set energy efficiency targets, increased their use of renewable energy, and made agreements to cut carbon pollution. These are the kinds of programs that states will be able to use to cut carbon pollution under this proposal.
  - o   47 states with utilities that run demand-side energy efficiency programs
  - o   38 states with renewable portfolio standards or goals
  - o   10 states with market-based greenhouse gas emissions programs
  - o   27 states with energy efficiency standards or goals

PROPOSED STATE PLAN DATES

June 30, 2016 – Initial plan or complete plan due

June 30, 2017 – Complete individual plan due if state is eligible for a one-year extension

June 30, 2018 – Complete multi-state plan due if state is eligible for two-year extension (with progress report due June 30, 2017

INDEX

A

access, 21, 23
accounting, 41, 60, 113
acid, 95
acquisitions, 113
adjustment, 36, 75
Administrative Procedure Act, 103
age, 18, 20, 21, 116
agencies, 79, 83, 84, 88, 96, 101, 106
agency actions, 84, 88
air pollutants, 5, 67, 83, 86, 94
air quality, 14, 111
Alaska, 39, 40, 44, 53, 55, 75
ambient air, 99, 109
appropriations, xiii, 92, 94, 100, 106, 107, 113
Appropriations Act, 106, 107
Appropriations Committee, 107
assessment, 11
assets, 9, 88
asthma, 116
asthma attacks, 116
atmosphere, 21, 22
authority(s), xi, xii, 62, 63, 64, 65, 69, 80, 84, 85, 93, 94, 98, 99, 101, 103, 105, 108, 109, 110, 114
automobile(s), 85, 93

B

base, xi, 11, 24, 30, 31, 62, 65, 71, 72, 87
base year, 30, 65, 71, 87
benefits, 20, 21, 72, 82, 83, 87, 88, 116
biological processes, 108
biomass, 4, 22, 33, 44, 52
boilers, 18
BTU, 22, 60
building blocks, vii, ix, x, xi, 2, 5, 6, 8, 9, 10, 18, 20, 28, 29, 30, 35, 36, 38, 50, 51, 62, 68, 73, 76, 78
building code, 46, 48
burn, 5, 12
businesses, 117

C

CAA, vii, xi, xii, 1, 5, 14, 23, 35, 62, 63, 64, 67, 68, 70, 72, 80, 84, 85, 86, 87, 91, 96, 111, 113
carbon, vii, ix, xi, xiii, 1, 3, 4, 5, 6, 7, 12, 15, 21, 22, 27, 28, 29, 35, 36, 37, 38, 52, 55, 58, 59, 60, 62, 63, 64, 74, 78, 83, 86, 88, 100, 104, 108, 111, 112, 113, 114, 115, 117
carbon dioxide, vii, ix, xi, 1, 3, 4, 5, 6, 21, 27, 29, 62, 64, 100, 104, 108, 111, 113, 115
carbon emissions, 3, 4, 5, 6, 7, 15

carbon monoxide, 83, 114
carbon reduction, vii, 1, 3, 6
case law, 68, 103
category a, 32
challenges, 18, 68
chemicals, 95
children, 116
cities, 117
classes, 81
classification, 111
Clean Air Act, vii, xi, xii, xiii, 1, 5, 22, 23, 29, 62, 63, 64, 65, 91, 92, 93, 94, 96, 98, 100, 103, 104, 105, 106, 108, 109, 110, 111, 112, 114
clean energy, 6
Clean Power Plan, vii, xiii, 1, 3, 5, 22, 60, 115, 116
climate, vii, x, xi, xiii, 1, 3, 13, 61, 62, 82, 83, 85, 94, 105, 106, 107, 108, 109, 110, 115, 116
climate change, vii, x, xiii, 1, 3, 61, 82, 83, 94, 105, 106, 107, 115
CO_2, v, ix, 3, 7, 8, 9, 10, 11, 12, 13, 15, 18, 21, 22, 24, 27, 28, 29, 30, 31, 32, 34, 35, 36, 37, 38, 52, 53, 59, 64, 65, 67, 70, 71, 72, 73, 74, 75, 77, 82, 83, 85, 95, 97, 100, 111
CO_2 emissions, ix, 3, 8, 9, 10, 11, 12, 13, 15, 24, 27, 29, 30, 31, 32, 36, 53, 67, 70, 71, 73, 74, 77, 83, 100
coal, viii, ix, x, xii, 2, 5, 9, 10, 11, 12, 15, 17, 18, 19, 20, 21, 22, 24, 25, 28, 29, 32, 36, 37, 50, 51, 62, 69, 72, 73, 74, 82, 87, 100, 104, 116
Code of Federal Regulations, 69
cogeneration, 32, 33, 52
combustion, 3, 4, 21, 32, 33, 52, 59, 95
commercial, 45, 97, 104, 112
common law, 107
competition, 11
competitive markets, 20
compliance, vii, viii, xi, 2, 3, 4, 5, 6, 7, 8, 10, 15, 16, 19, 20, 21, 62, 69, 72, 73, 77, 81, 82, 88, 104
compounds, 85

computation, 23, 36, 76
computer, 71
conference, x, 61
configuration, 18
Congress, xi, xiii, 1, 4, 22, 23, 62, 84, 85, 91, 92, 93, 94, 95, 97, 100, 101, 102, 103, 104, 105, 106, 107, 108, 109, 110, 112, 114
congressional hearings, 106
consent, 101
Consolidated Appropriations Act, 108
construction, ix, x, 10, 12, 14, 20, 23, 28, 31, 44, 45, 60, 65, 75, 87, 100, 113
consumers, viii, xi, 2, 9, 13, 15, 16, 48, 62
consumption, viii, 2, 17, 82
controversial, 106
coordination, viii, 2, 17, 19, 24
cost, viii, 2, 6, 8, 9, 11, 12, 13, 15, 16, 17, 18, 19, 20, 59, 67, 68, 81, 82, 83, 88, 96, 104
cost saving, 8
Court of Appeals, 69, 97
covering, 64, 77, 86
CPP, vii, viii, 1, 2, 3, 4, 15, 17, 19, 20, 21, 22
customers, 4, 24
cycles, 17, 24

D

damages, 83
data set, 30
degradation, 14, 111
demonstrations, 104
Department of Defense, 107
Department of Energy, 104
directives, xi, 62
displacement, ix, 28, 29
distribution, 17, 18, 31
District of Columbia, 40, 55, 58, 59, 60, 76, 87
diversity, viii, 2, 17, 18, 22
draft, 79, 84

E

economic activity, 65, 66
economics, 59
electric power sector, vii, viii, ix, 2, 15, 27, 29
electric system reliability, viii, 2, 19
emergency, 35
emergency preparedness, 35
emitters, xii, 64, 65, 92, 94
end-users, 45
energy, viii, ix, x, xi, xiii, 2, 3, 4, 6, 8, 9, 12, 13, 15, 16, 19, 21, 22, 25, 28, 29, 32, 35, 36, 39, 45, 46, 47, 59, 60, 62, 67, 74, 76, 77, 78, 80, 82, 87, 96, 99, 115, 117
energy efficiency, viii, ix, 2, 3, 6, 9, 13, 16, 19, 28, 29, 32, 35, 36, 45, 46, 47, 60, 76, 78, 80, 82, 87, 117
energy input, 22, 60
Energy Policy Act of 2005, 15
enforcement, 19, 98, 107
engineering, 18, 74
environment(s), vii, xiii, 1, 3, 20, 21, 22, 23, 25, 115
environmental effects, 81
environmental impact, 22, 67, 99
environmental policy, 8
Environmental Protection Agency, v, vii, ix, xi, xii, xiii, 1, 3, 22, 27, 29, 62, 63, 66, 73, 85, 87, 91, 92, 112, 113, 114, 115
equipment, 5, 11, 32, 36, 69
equity, 83
ergonomics, 112
evolution, 21
exclusion, 8, 98
executive branch, 80
Executive Order, 79, 87, 88, 114
exercise, 103
exporter(s), x, 29, 48, 49, 51
exposure, 116
extreme weather, viii, 2, 17, 19

F

factories, 45
families, 116
federal agency, 101
Federal Register, 22, 29, 59, 63, 70, 78, 80, 84, 85, 86, 87, 88, 101, 102, 110, 111, 112, 114
financial, viii, 3, 21, 104, 113
flexibility, viii, 2, 6, 7, 8, 9, 14, 20, 51, 68, 78, 99
food, 95
force, xiii, 92, 96
formula, 58
fossil fuel-fired electric generating units, ix, 27, 29
fossil fuels, vii, 1, 3, 4, 5, 21
funding, 46, 106, 107
funds, 106, 108

G

GAO, 84, 88, 89, 101, 102, 103, 112, 113
gasification, 32, 33, 36, 52
GDP, 65, 66
Georgia, 40, 43, 45, 53, 56, 75, 87
goal-setting, 74
grants, 106
greenhouse, vii, x, xii, xiii, 1, 3, 21, 22, 61, 63, 77, 82, 91, 92, 93, 94, 95, 96, 97, 98, 99, 104, 105, 106, 107, 109, 111, 115, 117
greenhouse gas emissions, xiii, 22, 92, 94, 95, 96, 99, 104, 105, 106, 115, 117
gross domestic product, 65, 66
grouping, 32
growth, 39, 40, 41, 44, 60, 71, 74
growth factor, 74
growth rate, 39, 40, 41, 44, 60
guidance, 94
guidelines, ix, 3, 5, 7, 9, 10, 13, 14, 27, 29, 64, 69, 81, 94, 96, 100

H

HAP, 70
Hawaii, 39, 40, 44, 53, 56, 75
hazardous air pollutants, 70, 83, 86, 111
health, xiii, 63, 67, 82, 83, 99, 115, 116
heart attack, 116
history, 84, 100, 111
homes, 45, 116
host, 34
House, 86, 101, 102, 103, 104, 105, 107,
    108, 112
House of Representatives, 103
human, 82
hydroelectric power, x, 28, 29, 33, 41, 44,
    49, 50, 51, 52
hydrogen, 83
hydrogen chloride, 83

I

image, 22
improvements, ix, 5, 11, 12, 14, 18, 21, 22,
    28, 29, 32, 35, 36, 45, 46, 48, 50, 73, 78,
    82
individuals, 80
industrial revolution, 22
industrial sectors, 45
industry(s), viii, 2, 4, 10, 12, 17, 23, 24
inflation, 65
infrastructure, 10, 19
insulation, 48, 78
investment(s), 20, 35, 82
Iowa, 40, 42, 53, 56, 75, 77
isolation, 50, 58
issues, viii, xi, xiii, 2, 4, 9, 15, 17, 62, 92,
    96, 110

J

Jackson, Lisa, 92
jurisdiction, 102, 103

L

landfills, 69
lead, 16, 48, 73, 94, 114
legislation, xiii, 77, 92, 94, 100, 101, 103,
    104, 105, 106, 110
legs, 17
light, xii, 64, 68, 91, 93, 97, 105
light trucks, xii, 91, 93, 97
liquid fuels, 4
livestock, 107, 108
Louisiana, 40, 43, 53, 56, 75
lower prices, 16

M

magnitude, 20, 51, 97
majority, 3, 18, 31, 32, 83, 101, 102, 109
management, 3, 107, 108, 113
manufacturing, xii, 91
manure, 107, 108
Maryland, 40, 42, 53, 56, 75, 87
mass, xi, 22, 35, 62, 78, 85
materials, 63, 78, 79
matter, 18, 82, 111, 114
median, 31
mercury, 19, 69, 83, 86
mergers, 113
metals, 95
methodology, ix, x, 8, 27, 29, 30, 37, 38, 41,
    46, 48, 49, 50, 58, 60, 77
Mexico, 40, 44, 54, 57, 75
mission(s), vii, xii, 1, 36, 63, 91
Missouri, 40, 42, 54, 56, 75
models, 71
modernization, 19, 25
modifications, 18, 23, 80, 111
Montana, 40, 43, 54, 56, 75
Montreal Protocol, 114

N

National Ambient Air Quality Standards,
    70, 85, 108, 109

national parks, 111
natural gas, vii, viii, ix, 2, 4, 6, 10, 12, 15, 16, 17, 18, 19, 24, 28, 29, 32, 33, 37, 52, 72, 100, 116
natural gas pipeline, 18, 24
nitrogen, 83, 111, 114, 116
nitrogen dioxide, 114, 116
nitrous oxide, 21, 108
North America, 19, 24, 31
nuclear power, vii, ix, x, 2, 3, 6, 12, 28, 29, 33, 34, 38, 44, 45, 49, 50, 51, 52, 59, 75
nuisance, 107

O

Obama, 3, 101
Obama Administration, 3, 101
Obama, President, x, xii, xiii, 61, 64, 65, 85, 87, 91, 115
obstacles, 102
Office of Management and Budget, 79, 88
officials, 63
oil, 32, 33, 52, 74, 95, 116
Oklahoma, 40, 43, 54, 57, 75
operating costs, 13, 14
operations, 9
opportunities, ix, 8, 9, 11, 18, 28, 29, 30, 32, 35, 41
organic compounds, 69
outreach, 63, 85
ozone, 82, 95, 114, 116
ozone layer, 114

P

parallel, 114
participants, 109
permit, 14, 65, 81, 93, 96, 97, 98, 99, 107, 109
personal communication, 112
petroleum, 95
plants, vii, viii, x, 2, 5, 10, 16, 17, 19, 20, 21, 24, 28, 31, 37, 51, 59, 68, 69, 70, 73, 74, 85, 86, 94, 100, 104, 115

PM, 111
polar, 24
policy, 10, 21, 25, 46, 79, 84, 95, 96, 103
pollutants, xii, 14, 16, 65, 67, 70, 82, 83, 86, 91, 93, 97, 98, 99, 108, 109, 110, 111, 116
pollution, vii, xi, xii, xiii, 2, 5, 7, 22, 23, 32, 62, 63, 67, 82, 83, 91, 92, 93, 94, 99, 111, 112, 115, 116, 117
population, 65, 66
portfolio, vii, ix, 1, 3, 7, 8, 19, 20, 22, 27, 28, 29, 30, 31, 36, 37, 41, 48, 59, 60, 74, 87, 117
power generation, vii, viii, ix, 1, 2, 3, 4, 5, 7, 8, 16, 17, 18, 21, 22, 28, 29, 35, 41, 44, 49, 72
power plants, vii, viii, x, xi, xii, xiii, 1, 2, 3, 5, 6, 7, 9, 10, 11, 12, 14, 15, 17, 18, 19, 20, 21, 22, 31, 37, 61, 62, 63, 64, 65, 66, 67, 69, 70, 73, 77, 85, 86, 91, 93, 94, 100, 104, 115, 116
precedent(s), 84, 88, 109
premature death, 82, 83, 116
preparation, 107
preservation, ix, 28
President, x, xi, xii, xiii, 22, 61, 62, 64, 65, 79, 80, 84, 85, 87, 91, 94, 100, 101, 102, 112, 113, 115
President Obama, x, xii, xiii, 61, 64, 65, 85, 87, 91, 115
presidential veto, 101, 104, 112
procedural rule, 85
producers, viii, 2, 17
proposed regulations, vii, xi, 1, 3, 62, 66, 67, 86, 113
public health, vii, 1, 3, 5, 67, 81, 83, 94, 99, 108, 109, 116
public policy, 20
pumps, 32

Q

quality standards, 111

R

radiation, 21, 22, 23, 110
ramp, 37, 74
ratepayers, 20
RE, 39, 40, 41, 42, 43, 44, 46, 51
reading, xii, 86, 92
recovery, 20
recreation, 111
regulations, vii, xi, xii, 2, 5, 14, 21, 24, 30, 31, 62, 63, 69, 77, 78, 79, 81, 87, 91, 92, 94, 96, 97, 99, 105, 106, 107, 110, 113
regulatory agencies, 79
regulatory requirements, 14
reliability, viii, 2, 3, 4, 9, 13, 16, 19, 20, 21, 24
renewable electric generation, vii, viii, 2, 6, 15, 17
renewable energy, ix, x, 12, 28, 33, 34, 35, 38, 39, 44, 52, 60, 74, 77, 78, 87, 117
renewable fuel, 68, 111
requirements, xii, xiii, 14, 19, 20, 30, 48, 65, 67, 69, 76, 80, 84, 85, 92, 93, 94, 96, 97, 98, 99, 105, 109, 110
resolution, xiii, 84, 85, 92, 101, 102, 103, 104, 106, 112, 113
resources, xii, 7, 8, 13, 24, 78, 92
response, 4, 16, 17, 24, 70, 84, 100, 103, 110
retail, viii, 2, 16, 46, 47, 48, 60, 87
retirement, viii, 2, 12, 18, 19, 23, 87
rights, 113
risk(s), x, xiii, 13, 23, 28, 33, 34, 44, 45, 49, 52, 59, 75, 87, 115
rules, 20, 64, 67, 69, 79, 80, 84, 88, 101, 102, 105, 112

S

safety, 63, 83
savings, 13, 16, 46, 47, 48, 60
school, 116
science, xiii, 115
scope, xii, 68, 92

security, 15, 35
Senate, 84, 86, 101, 102, 103, 104, 105, 107, 108, 109, 112, 113
services, viii, 2, 13, 19, 113
showing, 46
Sierra Club, 86
smog, 116
social costs, 83
South Dakota, 40, 42, 43, 54, 57, 74, 76, 77
spreadsheets, 38, 58, 59
stakeholders, 3, 79
State Implementation Plan(s), 72
steel, 95
storage, 17, 18, 100, 104
structure, 4
subcategorization, 81
sulfur, 21, 83, 85, 111, 114, 116
sulfur dioxide, 83, 111, 114, 116
suppliers, viii, 2, 60, 87
Supreme Court, 5, 64, 65, 85, 86, 94, 97
surplus, 24

T

target, vii, 1, 3, 8, 39, 40, 41, 46, 48, 77
technical support, 38, 58, 60
technology(s), viii, 2, 10, 12, 17, 68, 100, 104
temperature, viii, 2, 19
Title I, 108, 111
Title IV, 108
Title V, xii, 92, 93, 94, 96, 97, 98, 105, 108, 109, 110, 111, 114
tracks, 100
trade, 69, 72, 77, 108, 114
transactions, 19
transcripts, 87
transmission, 11, 15, 19, 20, 24, 32, 37, 74
transport, 96
transportation, 24, 106
triggers, 88, 96

U

U.S. policy, 7
United, vii, ix, x, xii, 1, 3, 4, 7, 10, 17, 24,
    27, 29, 31, 61, 64, 65, 66, 85, 88, 91,
    104, 112, 113, 115
United Nations, 64, 85
United Nations Framework Convention on
    Climate Change (UNFCCC), 64, 85
United States, vii, ix, x, xii, 1, 3, 4, 7, 10,
    17, 24, 27, 29, 31, 61, 65, 66, 88, 91,
    104, 112, 113, 115
universe, 70

V

variable costs, 16
vehicles, xii, 64, 65, 85, 91, 99, 107, 116
veto, 84, 101, 102, 104, 106
vision, viii, 2, 15
volatility, viii, 2, 17

vote, 101, 102, 105, 107, 112

W

wages, 113
waiver, 106, 107
Washington, 9, 40, 44, 49, 51, 55, 57, 63,
    72, 73, 76, 79, 87, 88
water, 108
water vapor, 108
weather-related outages, viii, 2, 19
welfare, 67, 81, 94, 99, 108, 109
well-being, 63
White House, 79, 112
wholesale, 16, 34
Wisconsin, 40, 43, 55, 58, 75
wood, 33, 44, 52

Y

yield, 48, 59, 82